The Supported Learning in Physics Project
has received major support from

ESSEX

LE
IN PHY
PROJE

The Open
University

D0334464

PHYSICS ON A PLATE

This unit was written by
Chris Barrett and David Sumner
with Geoff Auty and Martin Brown

009 989

Heinemann

The project is also supported by
The Department for Education and
Employment

THE SUPPORTED LEARNING IN PHYSICS PROJECT

Management Group

Elizabeth Whitelegg, Project Director, The Open University

Professor Dick West, National Power Professor of Science Education, The Open University

Christopher Edwards, Project Coordinator

Professor Mike Westbrook, Vice-President for Education, Industry and Public Affairs, The Institute of Physics

George Davies, Manager, College Recruitment, Ford of Britain

Geoff Abraham, Project Trailing Manager

Dorrie Giles, Schools Liaison Manager, Institution of Electrical Engineers

Martin Tims, Manager, Education Programme, Esso UK

Catherine Wilson, Education Manager (Schools and Colleges), Institute of Physics

Production

This unit was written for the Project by Chris Barrett, Institute of Physics, and David Sumner, Honorary Senior Research Fellow, University of Glasgow, with Geoff Auty, New College, Pontefract, and Martin Brown, North Eastern Education and Library Board, Ballymena, Northern Ireland

Other members of the production team for this unit were:

Elizabeth Whitelegg, Project Director

Christopher Edwards, Project Coordinator and Academic Editor

Andrew Coleman, Editor

John Coleman, Course Assessor

Alison George, Illustrator

Maureen Maybank, Unit Assessor

Julie Lynch, Project Secretary

Sian Lewis, Designer

Cartoons supplied by ABC Cartoons

ISBN 0 435 68844 8

The Institute of Physics, 76 Portland Place, London, W1N 4AA.

First published 1997 by Heinemann Educational Publishers.

Printed and bound by Edelvives, Spain.

For further information on the Supported Learning in Physics Project contact the Information and Marketing Officer, The Centre for Science Education, The Open University, Walton Hall, Milton Keynes, MK7 6AA.

1.1

	HOW TO USE THIS UNIT	5
1	INTRODUCTION	7
2	THE MENU	8
	Ready to Study test	8
2.1	Energy	9
2.2	What do we mean by hot?	11
2.3	What's cooking?	15
2.4	Hot dinners	16
2.5	Counting the calories	18
2.6	Metabolism	21
	Achievements	23
	Glossary	23
	Answers to questions	24
3	PREPARING TO COOK	26
	Ready to Study test	26
3.1	Hot pans and cold handles	26
3.2	Cooking under pressure	29
3.3	Into the frying pan	35
3.4	In the oven	38
3.5	Under the grill	39
3.6	The vacuum flask	44
3.7	The microwave oven	46
	Achievements	50
	Glossary	50
	Answers to questions	52
4	AT THE FACTORY	54
	Ready to Study test	55
4.1	Ice, water and steam	56
4.2	Frozen food	62
4.3	Melting and boiling	64
4.4	Freezers and heat exchangers	72
4.5	Food drying processes	75
4.6	Why is milk white?	77
4.7	Sugar solutions and perfect mirrors	91
	Achievements	95
	Glossary	95
	Answers to questions	97
5	CARRYING IT HOME	104
	Ready to Study test	105
5.1	To and from the shop	106
5.2	In the can	107
5.3	In the bag	116

CONTENTS

5.4	There's sugar in my cardboard cereal packet	116
5.5	In the yoghurt pot	118
5.6	Toast: a burning issue	122
5.7	Food colouring and eye-catching containers	123
	Achievements	130
	Glossary	130
	Answers to questions	131
6	**IN CONTROL**	**137**
	Ready to Study test	137
6.1	The need for control	138
6.2	Heating using electricity	140
6.3	Power revisited	143
6.4	The expanding cooking pot	145
6.5	Thermometers and thermostats	147
6.6	Timed to perfection	152
	Achievements	154
	Glossary	154
	Answers to questions	155
7	**CONCLUSION**	**157**
	RESOURCES AND FURTHER READING	**158**
	ACKNOWLEDGEMENTS	**160**
	INDEX	**161**

The SLIPP units introduce you to a new method of studying – one that you may not have used before. They will provide you with a way of studying on your own, or sometimes in small groups with other students in your class. Your teacher will be available to guide you in your use of this unit – giving you advice and help when they are needed and monitoring your progress – but mainly you will learn about this topic through your own study of this unit and the practical work associated with it.

We expect that you will study the unit during your normal physics lessons and also at other times – during free periods and homework sessions. Your teacher will give you guidance on how much time you need to spend on it. Your study will involve you in a variety of activities – you won't find yourself just reading the text, you will have to do some practical work (which we have called 'Explorations') and answer questions in the text as you go along. (Advice on how long each exploration is likely to take is given.) It is very important that you do answer the questions as you go along, rather than leaving them until you reach the end of a section (or indeed the end of the unit!), as they are there to help you to check whether you have understood the preceding text. If you find that you can't answer a question, then you should go over the relevant bit of text again. Some questions are followed immediately by their answers but you should resist the temptation to read the answer before you have thought about the question. If you find this difficult it may be a good idea to cover up the answer with a piece of paper while you think about the question. Other slightly longer or more demanding questions have their answers at the back of the section. You are likely to need help with these; this might be from a teacher or from working with other students.

It will be up to you to make notes on the physics you have learnt from this unit as you go along. You will need to use these notes to help you revise. You should also keep notes on how you arrived at your answers to the questions in the unit. It is important to show all your working out for each question and to set it out clearly, including the units at every stage. We try to do this in our answers to the questions in this unit.

Most sections start with a short 'Ready to Study' test. You should do this before reading any further to check that you have all the necessary knowledge to start the section. The answers for this test are also at the end of the section. If you have any difficulties with these questions, you should look back through your old GCSE notes to see if they can help you or discuss your difficulties with your teacher, who may decide to go over certain areas with you before you start the section or recommend a textbook that will help you.

The large number of practical explorations in the unit are designed to let you thoroughly immerse yourself in the topic and involve yourself in some real science. It is only after hands-on experiences that you really begin to think about and understand a situation. We suggest that you do some of these explorations with other students who are studying the unit and, when appropriate, present your results to the rest of the class. There are a large number of these explorations and it may not be possible for you to do all of them, so if everyone shares their results with others in the class you will all find out about some of the explorations that you are unable to do.

Your teacher will arrange times when the practical work can be undertaken. For health and safety reasons you must be properly supervised during laboratory and kitchen sessions and your teacher will be responsible for running these sessions in accordance with your school's or college's normal health and safety procedures.

HEALTH AND SAFETY NOTE

The unit warns you about any potential hazards and suggests precautions whenever risk assessments are required of an employer under the Management of Health and Safety at Work Regulations 1992. We expect that employers will accept these precautions as forming the basis for risk assessments and as equivalent to those they normally advocate for school science. If teachers or technicians have any doubts, they should consult their employers.

However, in providing these warnings and suggestions, we make the assumption that practical work is conducted in a properly equipped and maintained laboratory and that field work takes account of any LEA or school or college guidelines on safe conduct. We also assume that care is taken with normal laboratory and kitchen operations, such as heating and handling heavy objects, and that good laboratory practice is observed at all times.

Any mains-operated equipment should be properly maintained and the output from signal generators, amplifiers, etc., should not exceed 25 V rms.

Today we have access to a great variety of foods and different methods of preparation and cooking. There are many good cookbooks and several food programmes on television. Lenny Henry as Gareth Blackstock has even given us an insight, through the BBC situation comedy *Chef*, into the life of a top chef running his own business.

Gareth Blackstock is a chef with a spark of genius and a personality to match. He is tyrannical, egocentric, arrogant and irascible. As the story develops we see both how impossible he is to work with and how incompatible his choice of lifestyle is with his marriage. He is obsessed by excellent food and is seen spending many hours developing a dish until he is satisfied that it can not be improved any further and declares it ready to serve to others. At his level, chefs are often evasive when asked about the details of a particular dish. Most of us are content, however, to use some of the ever-growing number of recipes available.

We have always needed food to live. Long before the beginning of recorded history our ancestors made decisions about what to eat, how to eat it and whether it could stored for use in leaner times. At first their knowledge would have been based on experience, which would have included what they saw others doing or experiencing. One day when out foraging, an enterprising hunter–gatherer may have found a new kind of berry and decided to try it. The rest of the community would be told if there were no ill effects. If the berries were poisonous, hopefully the unfortunate taster would recover, or at least have time to warn the others.

In this way many discoveries were made. Our ancestors found that meat would stay edible for longer if it was cooled or frozen. Food that had dried out could still be eaten and would provide nourishment when there was nothing else available. Some meat and plants were more easily eaten and tasted better if they were put in the embers of a fire, or collected from the charred remains of a natural fire. As communication improved, that knowledge of cooking and preserving food could be shared and discussed more widely.

In our discussions throughout this unit we look at many aspects of food today, including its production, preparation and presentation.

In Section 2 'The menu' we look at various aspects of energy in relation to food. In Section 3 'Preparing to cook' we investigate the physics involved when you cook your own kitchen. Section 4 'At the factory' looks at some of the material properties important to the modern food industry, the main phases of water, and some of the industrial processes used. Section 5 'Carrying it home' examines some of the physical properties of the materials that we use to package our food. Finally, Section 6 'In control' looks at the methods of controlling temperature and measuring time when using modern appliances.

If you enjoy food and its preparation, we think that you will also enjoy studying the physics behind cooking, preparing and eating food.

INTRODUCTION

We all know that we have to eat and drink to stay alive. But why? Obviously we need energy for any kind of physical activity – walking, running, and so on. Just as a car needs petrol to keep it going, our bodies need fuel in the form of food and drink. We 'burn up' food in an analogous way to a car burning up petrol, converting the energy stored in our food into energy of motion. But we differ from cars in at least one important respect – cars don't need to be refuelled when they're not moving! Even when we are lying down resting quietly, or fast asleep, our body needs some energy, to keep the heart beating and the intestine contracting, and to maintain many other processes that normally we are not aware of at all (and we all know that just thinking about work is exhausting!).

In this section we examine what is meant by the term 'energy', the relationship between energy and what we call temperature, and the motion of particles in matter. We examine what happens when energy is transferred thermally from one object to another, and we look at the energy we require to survive.

READY TO STUDY TEST

Before you begin this section you should be able to:
- describe how matter is composed of atoms and molecules
- state the three basic phases of matter
- use scientific notation for numbers
- give examples of kinetic and potential energy, and be able to relate kinetic energy to the mass and velocity of a body
- describe the effects of heating.

QUESTIONS

R1 Express 2 803 486 in scientific notation.

R2 Use your calculator to evaluate $\dfrac{3.487 \times 10^{12}}{2.900 \times 10^{3}}$ and express your answer using scientific notation (to four significant figures).

R3 Evaluate $\dfrac{\left(8 \times 10^{-2}\right) \times \left(3 \times 10^{4}\right)}{4 \times 10^{2}}$ without using a calculator.

R4 Evaluate $(15.2 + 18.8) \times 10^{-5}$. Give your answer both in scientific notation to two significant figures and in decimal notation.

R5 Give two examples of kinetic energy and two of potential energy.

R6 What is the kinetic energy of a 1 kg bag of sugar travelling at 2 m s^{-1}?

R7 What happens when you heat something?

2.1 Energy

Energy is a very important concept in physics, but it turns out to be rather difficult to define! When we say that someone is 'energetic', the suggestion is that this person is always 'on the move' and has a capacity for getting things done. In physics too, an object is said to be energetic if it can do things. As a simple example, think of a ball. At rest on the ground, it can't do much; under these circumstances it is in a state of relatively low energy. You could, however, do things to the ball that would enable it, in turn, to influence other objects. You could, for instance, lift the ball up. If you then released it, it would fall and make a noise when it hit the ground. Alternatively, you could set it moving by kicking it. Then it could break a window, knock over small objects and do many other things. In both these situations the ball has energy.

Once the ball has been dropped or kicked, its capacity to influence other objects is fairly obvious. The term for this type of energy, which the ball possesses by virtue of its motion, is **kinetic energy**.

However, we believe that energy does not simply appear as the ball starts to move, but is there as a result of something that happened to the ball. In the case of the ball being dropped, this means that energy must somehow be given to the ball when it is lifted, and then stored in the ball when it is held above ground level. Because of its position, the ball has the capacity to 'do' things, although this capacity doesn't manifest itself until the ball is released. The ball had 'hidden' (or stored) energy as a result of having been lifted against the gravitational force. In general, energy that is stored in an object or a system is called potential energy. Our ball has stored energy by virtue of its position in a region where it is subject to the pull of gravity; this energy is called **gravitational potential energy**.

Where does this gravitational potential energy come from? The short answer is that it comes from the person doing the lifting. As they lift the object, some of their 'muscular energy' is transferred to the ball and into gravitational potential energy in the process. The source of the energy can be traced back further. For instance, the food we eat helps to keep us warm and is also the source of the energy used to raise the ball.

 How is food a source of energy for us?

Food is a store of energy, which is held as **chemical potential energy**. This is transferred into other forms of energy by the chemical processes within our bodies.

Furthermore, it is arguable that the majority of energetic process on Earth can have their energy traced back to the Sun. Plants trap light in the chlorophyll within their leaves and use it to convert the simple molecules CO_2 and H_2O into carbohydrates; the energy is therefore 'stored' as chemical energy. This is potential energy. When animals such as ourselves eat plants, some of it is eventually used by our muscles to create motion. This is kinetic energy. Figure 2.1 shows some examples of energy transfers.

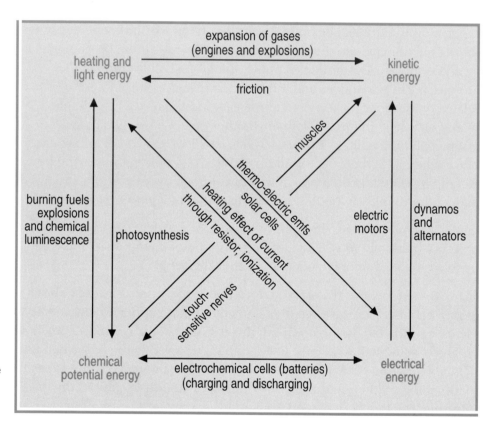

Figure 2.1
Some of the possible mechanisms for energy transfer

Plant material, fossilized in prehistoric times, is now used by us as a source of chemical energy to power our machines: cars convert petrol and diesel directly into motion; power stations generate electricity, which can then drive electric motors, such as the pump in our refrigerator.

A fundamental law of physics is that even though energy can be transferred into many different forms, the total quantity of it remains the same – we say that it is **conserved**. The **first law of thermodynamics** is a more detailed version of the law of **conservation of energy**. It gives us a definition of **internal energy**:

The increase in internal energy of any system is the sum of the work done on the system and the energy transferred to the system through heating.

We can write this as a word equation

increase in internal energy of a system = energy supplied through heating
+ work done on the system

2.2 What do we mean by hot?

If we say to you that an object is hot or cold, you will know what we mean at a practical level, but that will not necessarily help you give a scientific explanation of the terms 'hot', 'cold' or **temperature**.

 What is temperature?

For now, we might say that temperature is a measure of how hot something is. Unfortunately, we then end up in a circular argument, saying that a hot body has a high temperature.

But what happens if we take an object heated to 100°C, and place it in a sample of water at 80°C? We know that the temperature of the water will rise, and that of the object will fall.

 What temperature will they eventually reach? What is happening to the energy of the water and the object?

Eventually both the water and the object reach the same temperature, which will lie somewhere between the two original temperatures. Energy is always being transferred from the object to the water and from the water to the object. When they reach the same temperature the amount of energy passing in each direction is the same, meaning that now there is no net, or overall, change.

This gives us a useful starting-point in defining temperature. When two objects transfer energy, with no net loss or gain by either of them, we say they are in **equilibrium** and at the same temperature. If there is a transfer of energy and a net loss and gain, we say that there is a temperature difference between the two objects.

Although I say when two things are at the same temperature things get balanced, it does not mean they have the same energy in them; it means that it is just as easy to pick energy off one as to pick it off the other. Temperature is like 'ease of removing energy'.

(Richard Feynman, 1965)

So the temperature of a body is closely connected with the energy possessed by that body. If we were able to observe the atoms in any object at room temperature we would see them moving: just vibrating if in a solid, moving relative to one another if in a fluid.

 What kind of energy is this?

It is kinetic energy. (*Note:* The molecular kinetic energy that we are considering in this unit is the energy that we can associate with temperature. It does not include the energy of, say, the electrons spinning within the molecule.)

If we concentrate on gases for the moment, the molecules of a gas at a given temperature possess kinetic energy, but they do not all have the same amount: there is a distribution of energies. At any given temperature, all gases will have the same distribution of molecular energies. This is a remarkable feature, since it implies that there is a unique energy distribution for gas molecules at each temperature, regardless of the mass of those molecules. That statement can be turned round the other way to give a first 'definition' of temperature:

Temperature is a quantity that determines the way in which kinetic energy is distributed among the molecules in a gas.

In fact this definition has a much more general validity: it is true for solids and liquids, as well as gases.

Temperature is a quantity that determines the way in which kinetic energy is distributed among the molecules in a gas.

E **Exploration 2.1   Showing molecular movement**

30 MINUTES

Wear eye protection. Always stand while heating liquids.

Apparatus

- ◆ five beakers of water ◆ three tripods, gauzes and heat mats
- ◆ three Bunsen burners ◆ dropping pipette ◆ food colouring
- ◆ three thermometers ◆ two stopwatches.

Fill all five beakers to the same level with water, about two-thirds full. Place beaker A on a piece of white paper or card and allow beakers A and B to settle at room temperature. Heat the others until C is at approximately 60°C, D at roughly 95°C and E is boiling. (See Figure 2.2.) Allow C and D to settle once they have reached their temperature by turning off the Bunsen and leaving for a couple of minutes for the convection within the water to reduce.

While E is still bubbling, but with the Bunsen turned off, squeeze two or three drops of food colouring into the middle and time how long it takes for the colour to spread evenly through the water.

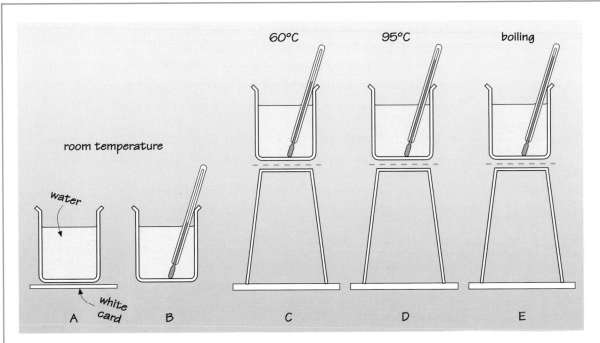

room temperature

water

white card

A   B   60°C   95°C   boiling
              C   D   E

Figure 2.2 Arrangement of beakers for Exploration 2.1

 Why should you introduce the food colouring as gently as possible?

The motion of the food colouring entering the water will produce some mixing. This is not particularly important for the boiling liquid but will have an effect on the others.

Now squeeze the same amount of colouring into beaker A and start the second stopwatch, make sure that you don't knock this beaker (*Note:* Beaker A is likely to take several hours before the colour is spread evenly, so you will need to come back at intervals to check this). Using the first stopwatch, time how long it takes for the same amount of colour to spread evenly through beaker D then beaker C.

Then, with someone stirring the water, add the food colouring to beaker B and time the spread of colour until it is again uniform.

Q1 What is the order in which the colour in each of the beakers became uniform? Explain why this is. ◆

Figure 2.3(a) shows a plot of the average molecular kinetic energy against temperature in degrees **Celsius** for a gas. The resulting graph is a straight line, but it doesn't go through the origin; in fact, the temperature corresponding to zero kinetic energy is −273.15°C. It would be much more convenient if the line went through the origin! We can do this by defining temperature in such a way as to generate Figure 2.3(b):

The temperature of a gas is directly proportional to the average kinetic energy of the gas molecules.

The temperature of a gas is directly proportional to the average kinetic energy of the gas molecules.

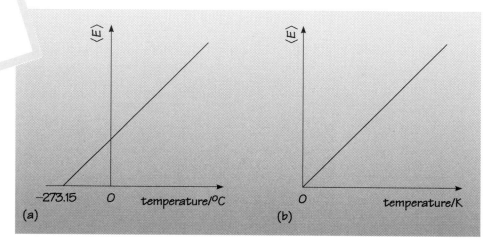

Figure 2.3
Average molecular kinetic energy against temperature for a gas with the temperature scales (a) °C and (b) K

For this definition to work we need to set up a new scale of temperature on which the zero point will correspond to zero average kinetic energy. Since kinetic energies can never be negative, this temperature must be the lowest limit of temperature – so-called **absolute zero**. The unit of temperature on this scale is called the **kelvin**, after the Scottish physicist William Thomson, Lord Kelvin (1824–1907). Kelvin is the **SI (Système International d'Unités)** unit of temperature. Its symbol is K (not °K). We can now redefine other temperature scales in terms of the **kelvin scale** – also commonly called the **absolute scale**.

$$0 \text{ K} = -273.15°C$$

The size of a unit on the kelvin scale is chosen to be equal to the size of a unit on the Celsius scale, so conversion from one scale to the other simply becomes a matter of adding or subtracting 273.15 (you can use 273 unless a high degree of accuracy is called for). Using the symbol θ for temperature on the Celsius scale, and T for temperature on the kelvin scale

$$\theta\,/°C = T/K - 273$$

Thus, for example,

$$127°C = 400 \text{ K}$$
$$27°C = 300 \text{ K}$$

and

$$-73°C = 200 \text{ K}$$

Q2 0°C is roughly 273 K. What are the equivalent temperatures to: (a) 50°C, (b) 50 K, (c) 1000°C, (d) 2000 K? ◆

So, provided *T* is measured in kelvins, we can write

$$T \propto \langle E \rangle \qquad\qquad (2.1)$$

where $\langle E \rangle$ is the average kinetic energy.

2.3 What's cooking?

It is Sunday morning. You wake, late, and, after a little tossing and turning, you realize that the rest of the household is already out of bed and downstairs. They are making breakfast. You can tell by the delicious aroma of fresh coffee, toast and frying bacon drifting upstairs. How do the molecules given off by the cooking food manage to reach you in your room? We know that they have moved from downstairs in the kitchen, up to your bedroom, and they have crossed the room and gone into your nose. The fact they have moved gives us a clue. In order to move they must have energy – kinetic energy to be exact. Where has this energy come from? The answer we found in the last section is that the molecules of the aroma have a finite temperature, and hence they possess kinetic energy. Let us look again at the relationship given in Equation (2.1):

$$T \propto \langle E \rangle$$

To have a full definition of temperature, we need to have a true equation rather than a proportionality. In fact, the most convenient way of writing such an equation involves turning the relationship round the other way and introducing a proportionality constant (which in this case is $\frac{3}{2}k$).

Equation (2.1) then becomes

$$\langle E \rangle = \frac{3}{2}kT \qquad\qquad (2.2)$$

Notice that Equation (2.2) connects a large-scale property of the gas (its temperature) to a property of its constituent molecules (their kinetic energy).

The constant *k*, known as **Boltzmann's constant**, has the value 1.381×10^{-23} J K^{-1}. The average kinetic energy of molecules in air at room temperature (about 300 K) is given by

$$\langle E \rangle = \frac{3}{2}kT$$

$$= \frac{3}{2} \times 1.381 \times 10^{-23} \text{ J K}^{-1} \times 300 \text{ K}$$

$$= 6.22 \times 10^{-21} \text{ J}$$

(*Note:* This does not depend on the phase of the substance.)

Q3 The mass of one molecule of oxygen is 5.32×10^{-26} kg. (a) What is the average speed of a molecule of oxygen in air at room temperature? Show how you reach your answer. (b) How much time would it take a molecule at this speed to cross a room that is 2.5 m wide? ◆

When someone is preparing a meal in the kitchen, we can often can smell the food cooking from other parts of the house, but the smells certainly don't travel at the sort of speeds you will have calculated!

 So why do smells take longer than this to travel?

The first thing to realize is that a given molecule doesn't travel straight across a room at more than 400 metres per second. In a very short distance it will collide with another molecule and change direction; in fact it will be continually changing direction, and will drift only very slowly away from where it started.

But if it is that slow, why do we smell the cooking as quickly as we do? The transport of the molecules from room to room will probably be due mainly to large-scale movement of air – convection currents and draughts.

2.4 Hot dinners

If you take a hot saucepan off the cooker, it cools down: energy is transferred from the saucepan to its cooler surroundings. If you touch the cold freezer compartment with a warm finger, energy flows from your finger into the metal. Does it ever happen the other way round? Why doesn't the saucepan become hotter and the surrounding air cooler? Observation shows that energy always passes from a hotter body to a colder; the opposite process has never been observed.

Experience tells us that if we place a cold can of cola next to a hot parcel of chips, then energy will pass spontaneously from the hot chips to the cold drink. Left long enough, the two will reach the same temperature. In this particular case the chips will end up too cold to be palatable, and the cola too warm to be refreshing. Figure 2.4 shows this situation.

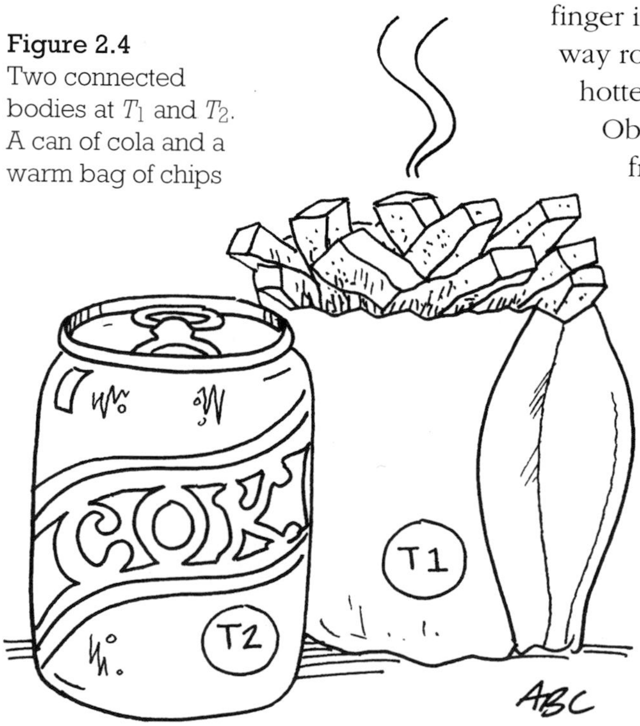

Figure 2.4
Two connected bodies at T_1 and T_2. A can of cola and a warm bag of chips

ABC

16

The hot parcel of chips is at T_1, hotter than the cold can of cola at T_2. After a very short time a small amount of energy, ΔQ, has passed from the chips to the drink. The amount is too small to cause any appreciable change in the temperatures T_1 and T_2. The total energy in this system consisting of the chips and the can of drink has not changed (we have already seen in the first law of thermodynamics that energy is conserved), but it is now distributed slightly differently, since the chips have lost an amount ΔQ and the drink has gained an amount ΔQ. Some property of the system has, however, changed in that the energy ΔQ has moved from the chips at a high temperature to the drink at a lower temperature. The property that has changed we call the **entropy** of the system:

$$\text{change of entropy} = \frac{\text{change of energy}}{\text{temperature}}$$

Our system consists only of the chips and the cola so when we consider the change in entropy of the system we need to combine the change in entropy of the chips with that of the cola.

$$\text{change in entropy of chips } = \frac{-\Delta Q}{T_1}$$

and

$$\text{change in entropy of cola } -\frac{+\Delta Q}{T_2}$$

so, putting these together gives

$$\text{total change of entropy} = \frac{\Delta Q}{T_2} - \frac{\Delta Q}{T_1}$$

Since T_2 is smaller than T_1, the entropy of this system has increased. When a change involves an increase in entropy we say that it is *irreversible* as it will not naturally revert to its original state.

Some time later the temperatures of the chips and the cola are closer. The equation for the total change of entropy still shows an increase, but this time it is smaller. The rate of increase of entropy continues to decrease until it reaches zero when their temperatures are the same. They will not change any further. However, energy is still able to pass from the chips to the cola and from the cola to the chips.

 Suppose some energy now passes from the cola to the chips while they are at the same temperature, what will be the change in entropy?

There will be no change in entropy as the entropy lost by the cola is the same as the entropy gained by the chips.

Such a change resulting in no change of entropy is called *reversible* and is equally likely in either direction.

 We haven't mentioned a process involving a negative change in entropy – why not?

As far as we know, none exist. A negative change in entropy would result from a cold object warming a hotter object.

We also know that internal energy cannot be changed completely into work. We cannot transfer the chemical energy in our food completely into kinetic energy by running. The transfers within our body also make us warm. Or, when fuel is burnt in a car, some of the energy gets transferred into energy of motion – kinetic energy – but there is always an accompanying rise in temperature, and we can never completely reclaim all of the energy that produced this temperature rise.

We have just described two ideas. First, that when two objects are in contact energy will not naturally pass in the direction from the colder to the hotter one. Second, that we cannot completely transfer internal energy into mechanical energy as some heating will always also take place.

These two ideas are combined to form the **second law of thermodynamics**:

> A spontaneous change is accompanied by an increase in the total entropy. For a change carried out under conditions of equilibrium, the total entropy does not change.

Because of the second law of thermodynamics, it is not possible to have a refrigerator that works spontaneously; we wouldn't expect the interior to get colder as the outside got warmer! The refrigerator is a type of heat pump, a device that uses energy to transfer energy in the 'unnatural' direction from cold to hot. We will look at refrigerators in more detail in Section 4.4.

SECOND LAW OF THERMODYNAMICS

A spontaneous change is accompanied by an increase in the total entropy. For a change carried out under conditions of equilibrium, the total entropy does not change.

2.5 Counting the calories

(Or, more scientifically, counting the **joules**.)

You may well be familiar with the way in which the energy content of foods is given in **calories**. The calorie is not a unit of energy used regularly in physics; the standard SI unit of energy is the joule. If you look on the back of most food packets these days you will find the energy value of the food given in joules and kilocalories. However, to confuse matters, the 'Calorie' (with a capital C) often used to describe the energy that we obtain from our food when we talk about diet is actually the kilocalorie (1000 calories). One calorie is equivalent to about 4.2 joules, so 1 Calorie (i.e. 1 kcal) is equivalent to about 4.2 kJ. To avoid confusion we will not use the term 'Calorie' (meaning 1000 calories).

A typical intake for someone in this country is between 8400 and 12 600 kJ (2000 and 3000 kcal) each day, and will vary considerably according to age, gender and body size.

This energy is used in three ways: maintenance (energy required to maintain normal body functions and conditions, for example breathing, blood circulation, body temperature and normal replacement of cells), growth (energy needed to synthesize and store new tissue) and activity (energy needed for moving the body and other objects, and for thinking).

Roughly half the energy provided by food is used in the physical activity of work and recreation, but obviously this proportion will vary depending on how active you are – a builder's labourer will need more than an office worker.

If a person takes in less energy than they require for growth, activity and body maintenance, extra energy will be used from fat stores in the body and the person will lose weight. On the other hand, if more energy is taken in than required, the excess will be stored as fat and the person will put on weight. One kilogram of body fat is equivalent to 30 000 kJ; so for every kilogram we want to lose, 30 000 kJ must be burnt up or cut out of the diet over a period of time.

Table 2.1 shows the average hourly energy requirements for various activities.

Table 2.1 Average hourly energy requirements (kJ) for various activities

	Women	Men
Cycling (moderate)	804	1072
Domestic work	641	837
Eating	370	469
Gardening (active)	1155	1541
Laboratory work (active)	502	670
Resting	358	425
Running (moderate)	1859	2478
Running (hard)	2897	3767
Sleeping	254	333
Squash	1930	2512
Walking (moderate)	703	938

(Source: Adapted from *Collins Gem Calorie Counter*, 1995)

Q4 Use Table 2.1 to estimate your typical daily energy requirement. ◆

FOOD AND FAMILIES 1800–1983

A rural British family of five persons in around 1800 would have consumed 380 000 kJ/week (i.e. 11 000 kJ/person/day). Of this, 37% of the energy would have come from bread, 45% from bacon, 9% from mutton and 9% from beer.

A poor urban British family of five persons in around 1900 are estimated to have consumed about 290 000 kJ/week, of which about half would have come from bread and flour; alcohol had been replaced by tea, which supplies only 1% of energy needs.

In 1983, an average British family of five persons consumed about 330 000 kJ/week, still less than the rural family of 1800, but that they would not have been involved in such physically demanding work. Also, we now utilize far more energy from fossil fuels, some of which helps to keep us warm and save us effort. The variety of foodstuffs is now much greater, and bread accounts for only 13% of energy intake.

Q5 Using a reference book such as the *Collins Gem Calorie Counter*, estimate your daily energy intake in kJ. Table 2.2 gives some examples of the energy content of a selection of foods. ◆

Table 2.2 Energy content of a typical portion of various foods

Food	Energy/kJ	Food	Energy/kJ
One eating apple	197	Low-fat margarine, per slice of bread	210
Baked potatoes (with skins)	569	Potato crisps (plain), per bag	550
Tomatoes (raw)	21	Biscuit	200
Brown bread	340	Vanilla ice-cream	1200
All-Bran (Kelloggs), with milk	700	Mars bar	1843
Cheddar cheese, 28 g serving	880	Coca Cola	180
Yoghurt, plain, 100 g	250	Diet Coca Cola	1.7
Fried bacon, per rasher	420	Tea	4
Butter, per slice of bread	250	Water	0

(Source: Adapted from Earle, 1994)

2.6 Metabolism

One very important process that needs energy is keeping ourselves warm. Warm-blooded animals such as ourselves consume quite a lot of fuel just to keep our body temperature constant, in our case at 37°C. The resting metabolic rate (the total energy transfer per second) of a warm-blooded mammal is about 10 times that of a cold-blooded reptile. So, in general, a reptile needs much less food than a mammal of the same size. Although this sounds like an advantage for the cold-blooded animal, there is a snag too: if insects and reptiles need to move rapidly they often have to bask in the sun first, to warm their muscles to a temperature at which the metabolic rate is higher.

When an animal is active, its metabolic rate (and, therefore, the heating of its body) can increase substantially. The metabolic rate of a flying bird is 10 to 20 times that of the bird at rest, and the increase in metabolic rate for flying insects can be 100-fold or more.

 How do animals stop themselves overheating?

Some animals use behavioural methods to reduce the likelihood of overheating; for example, reducing their level of activity, looking for shade or rushing into their burrows as their temperature rises too much. Many animals are nocturnal, emerging only at night to feed. Marine iguanas go into the sea to cool down and elephant seals throw sand over each other. Other animals have evolved physiological ways to cope to some degree. Dogs let their tongues hang out and pant, making use of evaporation. Elephants have ears with a large surface area to increase the level of energy transfer due to convection. People and many other mammals sweat, which again uses evaporation.

We know that the food we eat is used to provide energy for the body's maintenance, growth and activity. What are the mechanisms by which our bodies make use of the food? The first stage of the process is digestion, in which the complex structure of our food is broken down to simpler constituents. Carbohydrates, which are the body's prime source of energy, are broken down into glucose, which is readily transported to body tissues such as muscles. Within the cells of these tissues, the glucose is oxidized to provide energy.

Glucose in the blood stream is absorbed by the cells. In the liver and muscle cells, glucose that is excess to the body's immediate requirements can be converted to a substance called glycogen. When the body demands energy, this can be rapidly converted back to glucose. Longer-term storage is in the form of fat deposits.

A cell does not release all of the energy from a glucose molecule in one go, as it would not be able to harness it all. Instead, the cell carries out a much more gradual process, in which the potential energy in the glucose molecule is transferred eventually to 38 molecules of a substance called adenosine triphosphate (ATP). The cell is now able to use the energy stored in the ATP molecules to carry out its functions. Energy is transferred from ATP by combining it with water. Each ATP molecule can release 5.6×10^{-20} J to a future reaction, so energy obtained from each glucose molecule is $38 \times 5.6 \times 10^{-20}$ J $= 2.1 \times 10^{-18}$ J. If the energy of the glucose were consumed in one go it would release 4.7×10^{-18} J per molecule, so the advantage to the cell of using this gradual process is at the cost of extracting only 45% of the available energy.

 What happens to the other 55% of the energy that has become unavailable through the conversion of glucose to ATP?

This has gone into warming the cell and therefore helps to maintain body temperature.

Achievements

After working through this section you should be able to:

- use the concepts of potential energy and kinetic energy, and understand what is meant by 'conservation of energy' and 'equilibrium of energy'

- explain temperature in terms of the motion and energy of the particles in a body

- describe the concept of entropy and use the equation

$$\text{entropy change} = \frac{\Delta Q}{T}$$

- outline the way in which chemical energy in our food is used to provide the energy we need to exist

- describe how the absolute scale of temperature was established

- calculate average kinetic energy from

$$\langle E \rangle = \frac{3}{2} kT$$

Glossary

Absolute scale   The scale of temperature that takes absolute zero as its lowest point. Also known as the Kelvin scale.

Absolute zero   The temperature at which a perfect crystal has zero average kinetic energy.

Boltzmann's constant, k   A constant with the value 1.381×10^{-23} J K^{-1}.

Calorie   One calorie is the amount of energy required to raise one gram of pure water through 1°C. (One Calorie (with a capital C) is equal to 1000 calories.)

Celsius   The scale of temperature defined by the melting point and boiling point of water. (The same as centigrade.)

Chemical potential energy   A form of potential energy where the energy is stored within the structure of chemicals and is transferred to and from this form through chemical reactions.

Conservation of energy   Energy can be transferred, but the total quantity remains the same.

Conserved   After some process, a quantity is conserved if the total has not changed.

Energy   An object is said to possess energy if it can do work.

Entropy   Entropy is often thought of as a measure of order and disorder. The more disorder, the higher the entropy. So, as processes that cause entropy to increase are more likely to happen, we expect the Universe, and our kitchen worktops, naturally to become less ordered. For a process that involves an energy transfer, the change in entropy is given by

$$\frac{\Delta Q}{T_2} - \frac{\Delta Q}{T_1}$$, where Q is the amount of energy transferred, T_1 is the temperature of the hotter object and T_2 is the temperature of the cooler object. If the change in entropy is positive, the process will not naturally reverse – it is irreversible. On the other hand, if the change in entropy is zero (which will be the case if $T_1 = T_2$), the process is just as likely to occur in either direction – it is reversible.

Equilibrium   A state of balance between two opposing forces or effects, such that the system undergoes no total change.

First law of thermodynamics   The increase in internal energy of any system is the sum of the work done on the system and the energy transferred to the system through heating. Also known as the law of conservation of energy.

Gravitational potential energy
The energy of a body as a result of its relative position in a gravitational field.

Internal energy   The total energy associated with the motion and interaction of the molecules of a system.

Joule   The SI unit of energy. It is defined as the energy transferred when 1 newton is raised through 1 metre. For conversion purposes 1 calorie = 4.2 J.

Kelvin   The basic unit of the absolute temperature scale. 1 K is equal to 1°C.

Kelvin scale   See *Absolute scale*.

Kinetic energy   Energy due to an object's motion.

Second law of thermodynamics   A spontaneous change is accompanied by an increase in the total entropy. For a change carried out under conditions of equilibrium, the total entropy does not change. This law is a combination of two famous statements. They are: the Kelvin statement 'No process is possible whose only result is the complete conversion of internal energy into work through thermal contact' and the Clausius statement 'No process is possible whose only result is the transfer of energy from a cold to a hot body'.

SI (Système International d'Unités)   A coherent system of measures set up by international agreement. It is based on seven base quantities: metre (length), kilogram (mass), second (time), ampere (electric current), kelvin (temperature), mole (the amount of a substance), candela (luminous intensity). All other units, including all those that you meet in this and other SLIPP units, are derived from these seven.

Temperature   A quantity that determines the way in which kinetic energy is distributed among the molecules in a gas.

Answers to Ready to Study test

R1

$2.803\,486 \times 10^6$

R2

$$\frac{3.487 \times 10^{12}}{2.900 \times 10^3} = 1.202 \times 10^9$$

R3

$$\frac{\left(8 \times 10^{-2}\right) \times \left(3 \times 10^4\right)}{4 \times 10^2} = \frac{(8 \times 3) \times 10^{(-2+4)}}{4 \times 10^2}$$
$$= \frac{24 \times 10^2}{4 \times 10^2}$$
$$= \left(\frac{24}{4}\right) \times 10^{(2-2)}$$
$$= 6 \times 10^0$$
$$= 6$$

R4

$(15.2 + 18.8) \times 10^{-5} = 3.4 \times 10^{-4}$ in scientific notation, or $0.000\,34$ in decimal form.

R5

A person running and a ball falling both have kinetic energy. A loaf of bread has chemical potential energy and a tennis ball at any height above the ground has gravitational potential energy. You probably thought of other examples.

R6

$$E_K = \frac{1}{2} mv^2$$
$$= \frac{1}{2} \times 1\,\text{kg} \times \left(2\,\text{m s}^{-1}\right)^2$$
$$= 2\,\text{J}$$

R7

The temperature, phase or chemical nature of the material may change, and it may change shape, probably by expanding.

Answers to questions in the text

Q1

From quickest to slowest, we would expect you to have found the order to be: E, B, D, C, A. The boiling water is the most agitated and the colour should spread almost right away. The beaker being stirred should be next, but this depends on the enthusiasm of the stirrer. D, C and A were not visibly agitated when the food colouring was squeezed in; however, the water molecules were still in motion with a kinetic energy dependent on the temperature of the water. The higher the temperature, the more motion and the quicker the mixing.

Q2

(a) 323 K

(b) $-223°C$

(c) 1273 K

(d) 1727°C

Q3

(a) The full calculation is

$$\langle E \rangle = \frac{3}{2}kT = \frac{1}{2}mv^2$$

so

$$v^2 = \frac{2}{m}\frac{3}{2}kT$$

$$= \frac{3kT}{m}$$

and therefore

$$v = \sqrt{\frac{3 \times 1.381 \times 10^{-23}\,\mathrm{J\,K^{-1}} \times 300\,\mathrm{K}}{5.32 \times 10^{-26}\,\mathrm{kg}}}$$

$$= 483\,\mathrm{ms^{-1}}\ (\text{to three significant figures})$$

alternatively, as we already know that

$$\langle E \rangle = 6.22 \times 10^{-21}\ \mathrm{J}$$

we can rearrange

$$\langle E \rangle = \frac{1}{2}mv^2$$

to give

$$v = \sqrt{\frac{2\langle E \rangle}{m}}$$

$$= \sqrt{\frac{2 \times 6.22 \times 10^{-21}\,\mathrm{J}}{5.32 \times 10^{-26}\,\mathrm{kg}}}$$

$$= 484\,\mathrm{ms^{-1}}\left(\text{to three significant figures}\right)$$

(b) Now, to find the time taken to cross the room use

$$\text{speed} = \frac{\text{distance travelled}}{\text{time taken}}$$

$$v = \frac{\Delta x}{\Delta t}$$

$$\Delta t = \frac{\Delta x}{v}$$

$$= \frac{2.5\,\mathrm{m}}{483\,\mathrm{ms^{-1}}}$$

$$= 5.2 \times 10^{-3}\ \mathrm{s}\ (\text{to two significant figures})$$

Q4

There is obviously no single correct answer to this question.

Q5

Again, there is no single correct answer. A comparison between these two answers is more useful, but don't make any life-changing decisions on the basis of just these two answers!

Perhaps you have only ever cooked beans on toast; or perhaps you are capable of cooking and serving a four-course meal for a large family. Fortunately for those of you in the former category, we are not concerned with your cookery skills here. You may not know a skate from a skillet, but by the time you have finished this section you will know a lot of useful physics.

In this section you will study the conduction of heat energy through the materials of which cooking utensils are made, and learn about the heat capacities of these materials, find out how a pressure cooker can speed up cooking times, examine convection currents and investigate the radiation emitted by the grill in your kitchen. You will learn how a vacuum flask keeps food hot for long periods, and how a microwave oven can heat your food in such short times.

READY TO STUDY TEST

Before you begin this section you should be able to:

■ calculate the average kinetic energy of gas particles from the temperature of the gas

■ explain the terms 'atmospheric pressure', 'density', 'thermal expansion', 'electromagnetic spectrum' and 'wavelength'.

QUESTIONS

R1 Calculate the average energy of a particle of nitrogen at 20°C (use $k = 1.4 \times 10^{-23}$ J K^{-1}).

R2 Which has the larger wavelength, infrared or ultraviolet radiation?

3.1 Hot pans and cold handles

If you put a cold metal saucepan on a hot cooker, it will quickly get hot. Energy moves to cook the centre of a joint of meat or oven-baked potato by the same process. This process, known as **thermal conduction**, is also important in getting the centre of any food cooked.

We will now make the concept of conduction more quantitative. Look at Figure 3.1. Here we have a slab of material of surface area A and thickness L, whose faces are maintained at temperatures T_1 and T_2. Let Q be the energy that is transferred through the slab, from its hot face to its cold face, in time t.

If you were able to change each of the parameters in the diagram, how would you change each one to increase the rate of flow of energy from hot face to cold face?

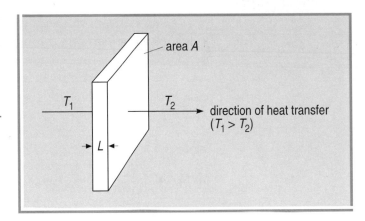

Make the surface area, A, larger; make the thickness, L, smaller; increase the difference in temperature between hot and cold faces; choose a material that conducts energy well, such as a metal.

Figure 3.1
The direction of the flow of energy through a material due to a temperature difference

 Express this mathematically.

If we assume that Q has a simple relationship to each of these parameters, i.e. proportional or inversely proportional, then we can write the following statements.

$$Q \propto A$$

$$Q \propto \frac{1}{L}$$

$$Q \propto T_1 - T_2$$

$$Q \propto k$$

where k is a property of the material called **thermal conductivity** (not Boltzmann's constant).

Putting these four statements together gives the energy transferred in time t:

$$Q = \frac{kA(T_1 - T_2)}{L}$$

Including time, t, in the equation gives

$$\frac{Q}{t} = \frac{kA(T_1 - T_2)}{L}$$

the rate of transfer of energy.

The value of k varies from material to material – large values of k indicate good conductivity. Most metals are good conductors of thermal energy, pure metals generally being better than alloys. Materials such as wood, glass, cork, plastics and fabrics are bad conductors. This is why kettles, saucepans, boilers and radiators are made of metals, such as aluminium, iron and copper, and tablemats are made of cork. Cloth, glass-fibre and cork are particularly poor conductors because they contain trapped air, and air is a very bad conductor of thermal energy (as in fact are all gases).

So why are gases poor conductors? Thermal conduction relies on the bonds between particles through which kinetic energy is passed from one particle to another. In gases the particles are not bonded and move freely and at random. Kinetic energy is transferred by collisions between particles, but collisions are comparatively rare.

Table 3.1 Values of k (in W m^{-1} K^{-1})*

Material	k
Air	0.24
Cotton cloth	0.03–0.04
Cork	0.04
Urea formaldehyde foam	0.03
Glass-fibre blanket	0.035–0.07
Glass	0.8
Glass (Pyrex)	1.1
Ice	2.3
Wood	0.08
Rubber	0.15
Solid plastics	0.12–0.55
Stainless steel	14
Aluminium	236
Copper	403
Iron	83.5
Chromium	96.5

* Thermal conductivity depends on temperature. Values given are at 0°C.

Thermal conduction takes place by three mechanisms:

1   In gases, collisions between molecules result in energy being transferred from the molecule with more energy to the molecule with less energy, although gases are poor conductors.

2   In solids and liquids, the motion of vigorous warmer atoms exerts forces on the colder neighbouring atoms so that they vibrate more vigorously too, and in this way energy is transferred along the bonds.

3   In metals, which are generally good conductors of thermal energy, there are **free electrons** that wander about within the material. When one part of a metal object – the base of a saucepan, for example – is heated, the electrons there move faster and farther. As a result they 'jostle' atoms in cooler parts of the saucepan, so passing on some of

their energy and raising the temperature of these cooler parts. This process occurs more quickly than conduction in a non-metal, which does not have free electrons.

Because electrical conduction is also due to the movement of free electrons, you might expect that good conductors of energy would also be good conductors of electricity. In fact there is a simple relationship between thermal conductivity k and electric conductivity s:

$$\frac{k}{s} = \text{constant} \times \text{temperature}$$

This is sometimes referred to as the **Wiedemann–Franz law**.

Answer the following questions using the values of k in Table 3.1.

 Why does the metal part of a fridge (the ice box) feel much colder than the plastic parts?

Because metal is a much better conductor than plastic, energy will be readily conducted away from your finger when you touch the metal (even though the plastic and metal parts are at the same temperature).

 If you are hiking, why is it better to have a stainless steel cup rather than an aluminium one?

Aluminium is a much better thermal conductor than stainless steel and therefore energy from the contents of the cup will be conducted more rapidly to the surroundings. The aluminium cup will be very hot to hold too! Stainless steel also keeps a good mirror finish, which reflects energy back into the drink.

 Why are the handles of metal teapots, kettles and saucepans often made of wood or plastic?

Wood and plastic both have very low values of thermal conductivity k. So almost no energy is conducted from the metal container to your hand.

3.2 Cooking under pressure

We inevitably try to find quicker ways of doing things, and cooking food has always presented a challenge. Traditionally there have been few ways of reducing cooking times. Increasing oven temperature works up to a point, but then the outside of the food may burn before the inside is cooked. Chopping food into smaller pieces does reduce cooking time (it is the technique used in stir-frying), but it also results in a different dish – the same is true of deep frying. It was the introduction of the pressure cooker that revolutionized mealtimes in many homes as it dramatically cuts the cooking times of foods that would otherwise need very slow cooking.

You are used to changes of state, for example ice melting to liquid water and this in turn boiling to produce steam. When any substance is changing state at its melting point or boiling point, while being heated or cooled, its temperature stays constant. Its temperature begins to change again only after all of the material has finished changing state.

 What is meant by boiling point?

The temperature at which a liquid changes to a gas at constant temperature.

This doesn't explain how we can smell the flavour of an ice-cream before we taste it. Some of the flavour has got up our nose and so it must be a gas, but the ice-cream is not at its boiling point.

 What is this name for this change? How does it differ from boiling?

This change is **evaporation** and, unlike boiling, it can take place at any temperature – and this temperature does not remain constant during the change of phase. We often use the term **vapour** for the evaporated gas.

In this section we will look at the effect of external pressure on the boiling point of a liquid, and how this is used in the pressure cooker.

Figure 3.2 shows a liquid that has been placed in a container and the air above the liquid removed.

 What will happen to the vacuum space after a short while?

Figure 3.2
Liquid and vapour in a closed container

It will fill up with molecules that have escaped from the liquid. These molecules will exert a pressure on the liquid and container.

To understand what is going on here we need to go back to our model of the moving molecules with an average kinetic energy represented by $\langle E \rangle$. Remember $\langle E \rangle$ increases with temperature. This means that the rate at which molecules can escape will depend on the temperature. Some vapour molecules will collide with the liquid surface and stick, so becoming part of the liquid again. The rate at which molecules return will depend on the concentration of the vapour. At any steady temperature these two processes will reach a balance. There will be a constant flow of molecules leaving the liquid (evaporation) and an equal flow returning. When this happens the liquid and vapour are said to be in dynamic equilibrium.

The pressure exerted on the walls of the container and the surface of the liquid by the collisions of the gaseous molecules is called the **vapour pressure**.

 Does the vapour pressure depend on temperature?

Yes, because the rate of evaporation depends on the average kinetic energy, $\langle E \rangle$, and therefore on temperature, the vapour pressure also depends on temperature. It will increase with increasing temperature.

Exploration 3.1   Checking vapour above hot water

Apparatus:

◆ beaker ◆ gauze ◆ tripod ◆ Bunsen burner
◆ heat mat ◆ water ◆ several long-handled metal
spoons that have been cooled in a refrigerator

20 MINUTES

Wear eye protection. Always stand when heating liquids.

Begin to heat the beaker of water. Hold the bowl of one of the spoons just above the water surface for a few seconds then check to see if there is any condensation. As the water gets hotter do this again. After doing this a few times over a good range of temperatures you should begin to notice a trend.

Q1   Why does more water condense on a spoon when the water is hotter? ◆

As the temperature of the water approaches 100°C, the vapour pressure rises until it becomes equal to the pressure of the atmosphere. At this point vapour doesn't just form at the surface of the liquid but bubbles are able to form within the water, and as they are less dense than the liquid they are able to rise to the surface and burst. Of course, we are familiar with this phenomenon as boiling.

 What happens to the temperature of the boiling point if the atmospheric pressure is higher?

The boiling point will now be at a higher temperature because molecules will need more kinetic energy for their vapour pressure to equal atmospheric pressure.

Solids also have a vapour pressure. Even within a solid, some molecules will have enough energy to escape and form a vapour, and the rate will also increase with temperature. The vapour pressure of most solids, however, is small because the molecules are more tightly bound together. Figure 3.3 shows what is known as a **phase diagram** of water.

The three lines on the phase diagram represent the three changes of solid to liquid, liquid to gas and solid to gas. Lines A and B represent the variation of the vapour pressure of ice and water, and you can see that they both change with temperature as we have discussed. An alternative is to consider these lines as representing the change of boiling point with pressure. Line C is similarly the melting point of ice, and it can also be seen to vary with pressure.

The point T where all these curves meet is called the triple point. At this temperature (0.01°C or 273.16 K) and pressure (0.61 kPa) water can coexist in all three states.

 Looking at the phase diagram for water, how does the melting point of ice change with pressure?

As the pressure is increased, the melting point of the ice decreases. For most substances the opposite is true, as this curve slopes the other way.

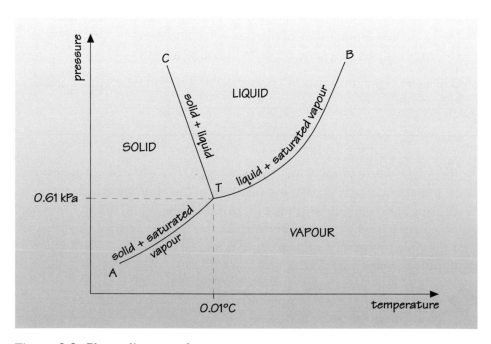

Figure 3.3 Phase diagram of water

Exploration 3.2 The cut that isn't

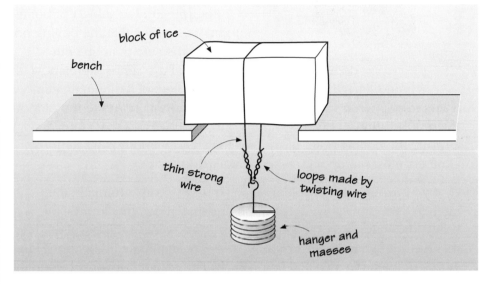

Apparatus:

◆ block of ice ◆ thin strong wire ◆ 1 kg hanger and set of 1 kg masses

Using Figure 3.4 to help you, set up the equipment. Use the thick gloves to stop the wire cutting into your fingers if you make any adjustments once it is under load.

> A wire under tension can snap or slip – wear eye protection and thick gloves. Place a cardboard box containing packing under the weights so that they fall safely.

Figure 3.4 Equipment for Exploration 3.2

Leave the equipment for the remainder of the session.

Q2 What happens? Try to explain this. ◆

Ice is an unusual solid in that it is less dense than its liquid form, as a result of the arrangement of molecules in the solid. For many materials, however, the solid form is slightly denser than the liquid form. We find that for these materials the melting point increases as we increase the pressure. In order to explain this we will introduce the rule known as **Le Chatelier's principle**:

> When a system is in equilibrium and something changes that would tend to destroy this equilibrium, then the system will adjust to oppose this change.

If the density of the solid form of a material is greater than the density of the liquid form, then when the material melts there will be an increase in volume. Increasing the pressure on such a solid opposes the expansion during this phase change, so higher molecular energies are needed for

> **LE CHATELIER'S PRINCIPLE**
>
> When a system is in equilibrium and something changes that would tend to destroy this equilibrium, then the system will adjust to oppose this change.

Sir Edmund Hilary with Norgay Tenzing on Everest – drinking tea in the western cwm after the successful ascent on 30 May 1953

melting to occur. This can only happen at a higher temperature so the melting point will increase.

On the other hand, the volume of a given mass of ice will be slightly greater than that of the same mass of water, so the effect is the opposite: the melting point is decreased by increasing the pressure.

Returning to the subject of boiling point, we can see that the boiling point of water is not an absolute quantity, but depends upon the pressure of the atmosphere above the liquid. Imagine, for example, the problem of a mountain climber trying to boil water for tea on top of a high mountain. At the top of Mount Everest the atmospheric pressure is only about 40% of that at sea level. As a result, the boiling point of water is lowered by about 20°C. Serious climbers must put up with lukewarm tea and coffee.

One way around this problem, which is also useful at home in the kitchen, is to artificially increase the pressure above the liquid – this is how a pressure cooker works. A pressure cooker is a thick-walled pan that has a lid sealed with a rubber gasket. A small hole in the top is fitted with a pointed pin attached to a weight. The amount of weight upon the pin determines the internal pressure at which the pin is lifted in the hole and the steam inside allowed to escape. Together the pin and weight form a crude pressure regulator.

 Why is a small hole best?

A larger hole would require a larger weight for the same pressure, which would be unwieldy.

Most pressure cookers have a set of weights that can be used to select the pressure and hence the cooking temperature. For mountain climbers, being able to raise the pressure to that at sea level means they can enjoy a hot cup of tea.

 What other advantage is there in cooking under pressure?

A pressure cooker

34

Using a pressure cooker also cooks the food more quickly, using less fuel. This is because it produces a higher cooking temperature which gives us a faster transfer of energy to the food.

With a great deal of rice and potatoes to cook, the provision of pressure cookers not only makes sense but is essential as the fuel they save far outweighs the relatively small disadvantage of bulk and weight. They were used on all major camps, and at camp 2. The rice and tsampa were pre-cooked before sending up to Sherpa climbers on the Face, saving time and fuel where it was most needed. [Tsampa is the staple of the Tibetan diet. It is yak's milk mixed with ground barley and tea.]

(Chris Bonington, *Everest the Hard Way*, 1976)

3.3 Into the frying pan

We learn by experience that when we cook the food gets hot. As physicists we can express that more scientifically – as energy is transferred to a body its temperature rises. Placing our full frying pan on the burning gas or hot electric element causes its temperature to rise and chemical changes take place in the food that we recognise as 'cooking'. Different foods cook at different rates and this section looks at one of the physical reasons for this.

One of the small mysteries of life to the non-scientist is why, in a treacle pudding, the pudding part can be pleasantly warm but the treacle burns the tongue. The explanation is that different food materials, like all other materials, need to absorb different amounts of energy to produce identical rises in temperature. When these different foods cool in your mouth you receive very different quantities of energy. Sometimes, as in the case of the treacle, sufficient to give you a nasty surprise!

The **heat capacity** of a material is the amount of energy required to raise its temperature by 1°C. It is also therefore the ratio of the amount of energy, Q, transferred to the object to the temperature rise that it produces.

Where T_i is the initial temperature and T_f is the final temperature, the heat capacity, C, is given by

$$C = \frac{Q}{\left(T_f - T_i\right)} \tag{3.1}$$

or

$$Q = C\left(T_f - T_i\right)$$

$(T_f - T_i)$ can also be written as ΔT. So,

$$Q = C\Delta T$$

If a given amount of energy produces a relatively small temperature rise, the heat capacity will be high; if it produces a relatively large temperature rise, this indicates a low heat capacity.

The heat capacity will depend on the nature of the material and also on how much of it there is.

It is more generally useful if a value of heat capacity is quoted for a given mass. We say that $c = \dfrac{C}{M}$, where m is the mass and c is the **specific heat capacity**. The specific heat capacity, c, is a property of the material, whereas the heat capacity, C, is a property of an object made from a material. Some values of specific heat capacity are given in Table 3.2.

Q3 Use the equation for heat capacity to produce one for specific heat capacity. ◆

Table 3.2 Values of specific heat capacity*

Material	Specific heat capacity ($J\ kg^{-1}\ K^{-1}$)
Copper	379
Iron	442
Glass	500–700
Aluminium	880
Stainless steel	440–470
Human body (average)	3470
Water	4190
Sea water	3900

* These values are at 0°C – specific heat capacities depend on temperature and tend to increase as the temperature rises (although the specific heat of water actually goes down slightly as the temperature increases from freezing to 35°C and then increases as the temperature rises further).

Notice that the average specific heat capacity of the human body is rather similar to that of water. This is not surprising, as the human body contains 60% water! In fact the specific heat capacity is lower than that of water, because the body contains air (in the lungs for example), and the walls of cells have a lower specific heat capacity than water.

Q4 If a 60 kg woman ate food of energy value 7500 kJ in a day and all the energy was used to raise her temperature, how large would that rise be? ◆

Even allowing for energy that is stored, we have a lot of energy to get rid of! In fact the temperature of the body is very closely regulated, and the body has various mechanisms for controlling the amount of heat energy that is lost. Some heat energy loss is by conduction and **convection** (see below) and some by the important process of evaporation – you will know that you sweat much more on a hot day, as the evaporation of sweat cools the body.

Let's now turn our attention to saucepans: we can apply our understanding of heat capacity to these too.

Q5 My cast iron frying pan weighs 1.2 kg. If 0.2 kg of this is the handle, which stays reasonably cool, and the rest heats up to an even temperature, how much extra energy will it have absorbed when it reaches the boiling point of vegetable oil (say 300°C) from room temperature? Why will the whole of the pan *not* heat up to an even temperature? ◆

 When you are cooking vegetables, why is it quicker if you put a lid on the saucepan?

If there is no lid, more water will evaporate, and much of the energy going into the saucepan will be 'wasted', as the vapour escapes. There will also be a slightly higher pressure in the pan with a lid on, so there will be a pressure cooker effect.

Before going on to the next section, take a look at Exploration 3.3 overleaf.

3.4 In the oven

Not all cooking has to be done in a pan. To account for oven cooking we need to look at a different method of energy transfer – convection.

Conduction doesn't involve the motion of molecules over large distances. In convection, however, the molecules of the transferring material move along with the energy – convection is the flow of energy through a fluid from places of higher temperature to places of lower temperature by movement of the fluid itself. When a fluid, such as air or water, is in contact with something at a higher temperature than itself, the temperature of the fluid will rise and (usually) it will expand. As it expands, its density decreases and it rises, a bit like a cork rising through water. The surrounding cooler fluid then falls to take the place of the rising warmer fluid; we say that a convection current has been set up.

Only liquids and gases can transfer energy by convection because only in these materials can the molecules move over large distances – in fact, convection is the usual method by which energy travels through fluids.

 What advantage does a fan oven have over a conventional oven?

Left to itself, hot air will rise to the top of the oven making the top shelf the hottest. A fan oven sets up a forced circulation, which produces a much more even temperature throughout the oven.

Read the following quotation from the section on saucepans in Delia Smith's *Complete Illustrated Cookery Course*.

Heavy-gauge aluminium

Not quite so glamorous as the others to look at, they offer all-round reliability and a good, even conducting of heat.

Enamelled cast ironware

These are very heavy and for this reason they hold the heat extremely well – so a much lower heat is needed to keep up a gentle simmer … I have found that sauces tend to stick and catch if I'm in a hurry and haven't kept the heat as low as it should be.

Stainless steel

I know one or two professional cooks who prefer these to anything else, especially now that the bases can be made with layers of steel, copper and aluminium which, sandwiched together, prove an excellent conductor of heat. I have found, though, that the contents of the pan nearest the edges (say while boiling milk or making a sauce) get hot quicker than the centre, which means that cooks in a hurry will regularly find the edges of the pan are scorched.

(Delia Smith, 1989)

Do Delia's opinions of the pans' performances agree with the physics principles involving mass, specific heat and thermal conductivity that you have just studied?

Rewrite Delia Smith's account of saucepans discussing the different contributions of mass, specific heat and thermal conductivity.

Alternatively, do the same for the following passage from Le Creuset's sales material.

Cast iron is a very energy efficient material and you will find, once hot, that you require only a low heat setting to maintain a good cooking performance … for some recipes, once hot the pan can be removed from the heat leaving the food to cook in its own heat.

Le Creuset has its own all round heat retaining 'blanket'. Because the base, side walls and lid are all of the same quality and thickness of cast iron there are no areas where heat can be lost rapidly. Heat is lost very slowly from cast iron meaning it can be taken to the table safe in the knowledge that food will be kept hot for some considerable time.

Have you ever tasted baked Alaska? On the outside is hot, crisp and crunchy meringue, yet, amazingly, on the inside is ice-cream showing no sign of melting – until you eat it. How do they do that? It is simple physics, but can you explain it? Exploration 3.4 overleaf shows you how to make baked Alaska. The first part, making the sponge, is optional – you could obtain ready-made sponge if you prefer (it needs to be approximately 20 cm diameter and 2–3 cm thick).

3.5 Under the grill

Stone-age people may have became aware of fire as a natural phenomenon, as bush and forests burned in dry weather (possibly as a result of lightning strikes). They may have used it initially to keep warm. Perhaps, in the aftermath of bush fires, they found animals that had died and been roasted in the fire, and their natural curiosity led them to eat their find. Fire was the primary source of cooking for thousands of years, until electricity was discovered, and it is a complex phenomenon. The fuel, wood or coal, and the gases it releases burn, emitting light and energy in the **infrared** wavelengths. This is absorbed by the food being cooked. The burning gases, which we see as flames, are very hot, so a pot, or piece of meat, suspended in the flames will also take up energy by contact with these burning gases (Figure 3.5).

Most recently we have developed the microwave oven as a means of rapidly heating food. It is unusual as a source of energy in that it relies on a very narrow band of wavelengths of radiation.

Baked Alaska

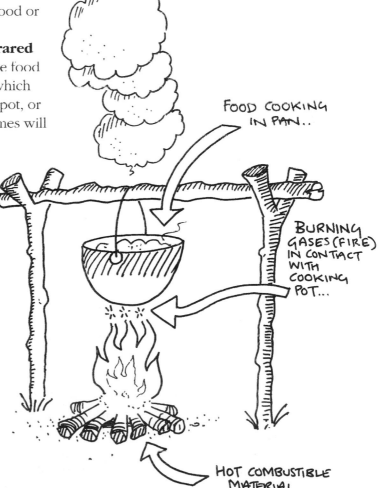

FOOD COOKING IN PAN..

BURNING GASES (FIRE) IN CONTACT WITH COOKING POT...

HOT COMBUSTIBLE MATERIAL...

Figure 3.5   The cooking fire

Exploration 3.4 Baked Alaska

40-50 MINUTES
preparation and cooking
plus 1 hour cooling time

Part 1 Making the sponge

Apparatus and ingredients:

- ◆ oven ◆ electric food mixer ◆ sieve ◆ 20 cm diameter baking tin
- ◆ wire cooling rack ◆ 150 g castor sugar ◆ 150 g soft butter or margarine
- ◆ three large eggs ◆ 250 g self-raising flour ◆ 5 cm^3 vanilla essence
- ◆ 20 cm^3 milk ◆ 3 cm^3 baking powder

Set the oven to 180°C. Beat the sugar and butter or margarine. Separate the eggs – keep the whites for the meringue and add the yolks to the sponge mix by beating them in. Beat in the vanilla essence and milk. Sieve the flour and baking powder into the mixture and fold in. Grease the baking tin and pour in the mixture. Put in the oven and bake for about 20 minutes, until it is well risen, golden brown, firm to the touch and beginning to shrink away from the tin. Turn out and cool on a wire rack.

Part 2 Making the baked Alaska

Apparatus and ingredients:

30 MINUTES
preparation and cooking
plus 30 minutes
eating and clearing up

- ◆ oven ◆ freezer (or freezer part of fridge) ◆ electric food mixer
- ◆ fruit or fruit jam (for example, 100 g fresh raspberries, 50 g blackcurrant jam or a 300 g can of tinned peaches, drained) – ideally the fruit should not be very sweet and have a sharp taste ◆ 500 cm^3 vanilla ice-cream
- ◆ three egg whites (you can use the ones left over from making the sponge)
- ◆ 150 g castor sugar ◆ flat ovenproof dish (20 cm diameter)

Heat the oven to 220°C. Keep the ice-cream as cool as possible as it must not melt when it touches the sponge. For best results, keep the sponge and fruit in the fridge before assembling the baked Alaska. Make the meringue by whisking the egg whites in a clean bowl until they are firm and fluffy. Whisk in half the sugar and continue whisking until the egg whites are firm again. Gently fold in the remaining sugar. Place the sponge in a flat ovenproof dish. Spread the jam or fruit over the sponge. Put the ice-cream in a solid lump in the middle of the cake – if you need to shape it to fit the cake use a bowl, but make sure that there is at least 2 cm of sponge showing all the way around. Cover the ice-cream with meringue. Take care that no ice-cream is showing and try to cover it all to a depth of at least 1 cm. Put the cake immediately in the hot oven and cook for 5 minutes, or until the meringue begins to brown.

Remove from the oven and eat immediately! One cake should serve at least six people, so be ready to share it – it won't keep very well. Coffee helps to wash it down.

Explain the physics behind what happened as you cooked the baked Alaska. If you have access to a video camera you could try making a video in the style of the BBC programme *How do they do that?*, recording your culinary adventures.

We will look first at the earliest method of generating energy for cooking – the fire. Jean Auel, in the third of her novels about life in prehistoric times (*The Mammoth Hunters*), writes:

Ayla watched Nezzie make the fire, idly at first, not paying much attention, but then she found herself intrigued. She knew, but had not really thought about it before, that they did not have many trees. They burned bone for fuel, and bone did not burn very easily. Nezzie had produced a small ember from another fireplace, and with it set fire to some fluff from the seed pods of fireweed collected for tinder. She added some dried dung, which made a hotter and stronger flame, and then small shavings and chips of bone. They did not catch hold well.

Nezzie blew at the fire to keep it going while she moved a small handle the young woman had not noticed before. Ayla heard a slight whistling sound of wind, noticed a few ashes blowing around, and saw the flame burn brighter. With the hotter flame, the bone chips began to singe around the edges, then burst into flame. And Ayla suddenly realized the source of something that had been nagging at her, something she had barely noticed but that had bothered her ever since she arrived at the Lion Camp. The smell of smoke was wrong.

(Jean Auel, 1986, p. 174)

E ▶ **Exploration 3.5   Colour and temperature**

10 MINUTES

Look carefully at a coal or wood fire (a gas fired, coal effect fire will also do). What is its colour: (a) when cold, (b) as it begins to burn, (c) when burning fully?

Where is the fire hottest, at the outside or deep inside? Look at the surfaces of the embers at the outside of the fire, and at the embers deep inside the fire. Which are glowing most brightly? Can you see any surface detail on the embers deep in the fire?

An electric grill or hotplate changes visibly as it is heated. At room temperature the metal tube enclosing the heating element, or the wire of an open element, will appear black (due to oxidized metal on its surface). As it warms above room temperature, you would at first notice no visible change, but if you held your hands close you would become aware of warmth on your skin. As the temperature increases, you would sense in this way that more energy is being emitted – your skin would feel warmer. Eventually the element will begin to glow, dull red at first, then bright cherry red, and eventually orange. By this time the thermal energy sensed by your skin would be unbearable. Indeed, experience of cooking tells us that a piece of animal flesh placed near the element would rise in temperature and undergo the chemical and physical changes we recognize as cooking.

Any object, even one we would regard as being very cold, is emitting electromagnetic radiation. The radiation does not occur at a single wavelength, but over a range of wavelengths, as shown in Figure 3.6. The total range of wavelengths is enormous in each case. At 700 K, significant energy is emitted from about 20 μm in far infrared to about 100 nm in the far ultraviolet. At long wavelengths very little energy is radiated. The intensity of this emitted energy increases with decreasing wavelength to a peak, and then falls rapidly. At very low temperatures the peak will be of long wavelength, and hence low frequency. As the temperature rises, so the wavelength of the peak radiation becomes shorter and shorter (see Figure 3.6). The wavelength of the peak can be related to the temperature by **Wein's displacement law**:

$$\lambda_{\max} = \frac{2.898 \times 10^{-3} \, \mathrm{m\,K}}{T}$$

This is exactly true only for objects that have become known by the term **black body**. A black body is a theoretical ideal body, which in principle would absorb all radiation falling upon it and, as we will see, would emit the maximum possible radiation for its temperature.

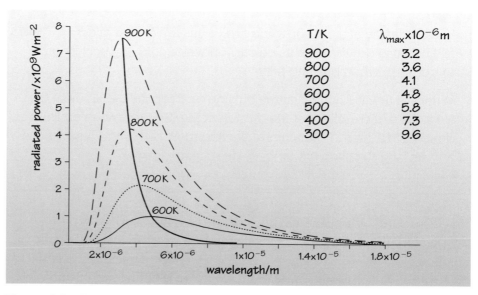

Figure 3.6 Graph showing the power of the radiation emitted from a black body at different temperatures

Exploration 3.6 Making a black body

5 MINUTES

Apparatus:

- ◆ empty baked bean can ◆ tin foil ◆ elastic band
- ◆ sharp pencil

Take a clean and empty baked bean can with the top cleanly removed, and fix a piece of aluminium foil over the open end with an elastic band. Using a sharp pencil, punch a small hole, about 2 mm diameter, in the tin foil. Look at the hole. Does it appear as shiny as the metal from which the inside of the can is made?

Figure 3.7 shows what is happening to light within our black body. There is no source of light inside the can, so any light we see within the hole must come from outside, and be reflected back outside through the hole. But in order for this to happen it will have been reflected several times. If, at each reflection, say only 80% of the light is reflected, after one reflection the light intensity will be 80% of that of a ray that entered the hole. After two reflections the light intensity will be 64% (because $0.8 \times 0.8 = 0.64$ or 64%), and so on.

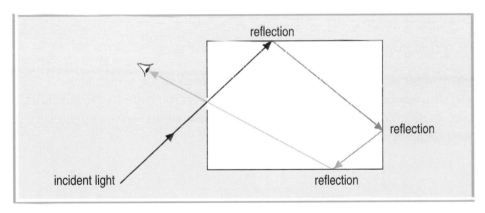

Figure 3.7 A black body

Q6 What will be the intensity after 10 reflections? ◆

So, even though the inside of the can is highly reflective, the absorption of light that takes place at each reflection reduces the amount of energy emerging. Blackening the inside of the can, say with soot or black paint, will reduce the emerging radiation enormously.

Q7 What will be the intensity after 10 reflections if at each reflection only 10% of the radiation is reflected? ◆

The surfaces of stars, and space itself, can be considered to be black bodies. On Earth, the interior of a coal fire is close to being a true black body.

Q8 Calculate λ_{max} for: (a) a body at room temperature (300 K), (b) the Sun (5800 K). ◆

Q9 An electric grill has a λ_{max} of 1.5 μm, what is its temperature? Sketch its black body curve. Humans can see wavelengths out to about 700 nm, use your sketch to explain why we see the grill glowing dull red. ◆

We can also calculate just how much energy is being radiated. This also related to the temperature by **Stefan's Law**:

$$P = \sigma A T^4$$

where P = power of radiation emitted, σ = Stefan's constant, A = surface area and T = surface temperature.

Q10 The grill in Question 9 has an effective area of 0.001 m². What is the total radiant energy, assuming that it is a perfect black body? ($\sigma = 5.67 \times 10^{-8}$ J s^{-1} m^{-2} K^{-4}.) By what other mechanisms would the grill element also lose energy? What would this loss do to the radiated energy? ◆

3.6 The vacuum flask

We also took a number of Thermos flasks ranging in size from one pint drink size to almost three pint food containers and used with a little forethought these too saved time, effort and valuable fuel at Camp 2 and above.

(Chris Bonington, *Everest the Hard Way*, 1976)

You will no doubt be familiar with the **vacuum flask**, which is used to keep liquids hot or cold (see Figure 3.8). It is often called a Dewar flask, after its inventor, or a Thermos flask, the name of the first commercially produced vacuum flask.

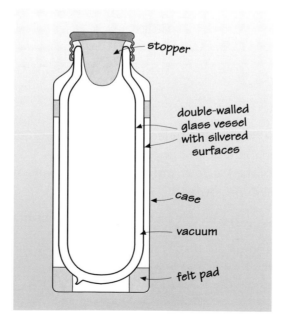

Figure 3.8 A vacuum flask

JAMES DEWAR (1842–1923)

James Dewar was typical of the physical scientists of his day in that he was interested in all fields of science – fields that today have become broken into specializations, such as chemistry and physics. He was exceptional in being able to make great contributions across such a wide range of subjects.

Dewar was an able student, and graduated with a degree in chemistry. During a ten year period at the University of Edinburgh, first as an assistant then as lecturer, he became interested in organic chemistry, and particularly in the then unresolved structure of benzene. Using brass models of carbon with its known number of bonds, he determined seven possible structures for benzene, including the one attributed to Kekulé, which forms the basis for our modern structure of the molecule. He followed this work with studies on the effect of light on animals, and on the production of a vacuum. It was while investigating the absorption of hydrogen gas by the metal palladium that Dewar devised a calorimetric apparatus that included a brass, double-walled, evacuated chamber, which he devised to give good thermal isolation of his experiment.

James Dewar holding a vacuum flask

Upon being offered the post of Fullerian Professor at the Royal Institution he continued the work of his predecessor, Michael Faraday, on the isolation and liquefaction of gases. It was during this period that he began giving Friday evening lectures, which became justly famous.

As part of his work on gaseous liquefaction he continued to improve the original brass vacuum flask, having it made from blown glass, adding a small quantity of charcoal to absorb the remaining gas left after evacuation, and depositing a thin layer of silver to reduce radiative losses. He never patented the idea of the vacuum flask, and it was a German company that developed the idea of the 'Thermos Flasche' into an important industry.

Dewar also investigated the properties of materials at low temperature, including the resistance of metals. As the first person to liquefy hydrogen, he was in an excellent position to study this property at temperatures down to its boiling point of 20 K. In 1908, Kammerlingh Onnes liquefied helium, and went on to win a Nobel prize for his discovery that the resistance of mercury would fall to zero (superconductivity) at such temperatures.

After the First World War, Dewar's research turned away from cryogenics, and investigated surface tension and the properties of soap bubbles and films.

(Source: Adapted from *Chambers Concise Dictionary of Scientists*, 1990)

Is a vacuum flask designed to prevent energy from transferring out or from transferring in?

A good design should work to keep cold things cold or to keep hot things hot, i.e. to prevent energy from moving either way.

The vacuum flask is designed so that energy losses or gains are reduced to an absolute minimum. The flask has double glass walls with a vacuum between the walls. With very little air (at a pressure less than a thousandth of atmospheric pressure), there can be hardly any conduction or convection. The slight energy loss that does occur takes place by conduction up the walls and through the stopper.

There is a third way in which energy can be transferred here – by electromagnetic radiation. Some energy can be transferred across the vacuum gap by the transmission of photons of electromagnetic energy. In the vacuum flask, this is reduced by coating the glass surfaces with a highly reflective coating such as silver or aluminium.

3.7 The microwave oven

The **microwave** oven is now a very common means of heating food. Most microwave ovens operate at a frequency of about 2.45 GHz (corresponding to a wavelength of 12.2 cm). Microwave energy of this frequency is produced in a vacuum tube known as a **magnetron**, which was originally developed for use in radar. The microwave energy is radiated into the cooking chamber. The chamber of the microwave oven is actually a resonant cavity – this is because it is about the same order of size as the wavelength – and it is in the form of a metal box with conducting walls. **Standing waves** are therefore present as in a stretched string, or an organ pipe. (You will find out more about standing waves in the SLIPP unit *Physics, Jazz and Pop.*) In the case of the oven, the standing waves occur in the three dimensions of the box. The door of the oven is made with perforated metal to allow us to see the food cooking, but the holes are too small to allow the microwave energy to escape.

Typically microwave ovens have a rotating turntable on which the food can sit. As the table rotates, the food passes in and out of the **antinodes**. This can be observed if a tray of water is placed in the oven. When the water is hot, the part of the water passing through an antinode boils.

A microwave oven

Why is the food heated by the microwave energy? The reason is that the microwave field causes the molecules of water to rotate or tumble.

Small differences in the electronic distributions in water molecules result in the oxygen atoms having a slight negative charge, and the hydrogen atoms a slight positive charge. This results in what is known as an electric **dipole moment**. As the microwave electric field rapidly changes direction, the electric dipoles attempt to align themselves with it, and so begin to rotate. The electric dipole moment has another effect. Hydrogen atoms of one molecule are *also* attracted to the oxygen atoms of another water molecule – this attraction is called the hydrogen bond. Any tumbling of a water molecule will tend to be resisted by the hydrogen bonds. As these bonds are broken and reformed, energy is exchanged into molecular vibrations.

Hydrogen atoms of one molecule are therefore attracted to the oxygen atoms of another molecule – this attraction is called a hydrogen bond. Any tumbling of a water molecule due to the microwave field will tend to be resisted by the hydrogen bonds – this will damp out the motion, with the energy exchanged into molecular vibrations. Again, the temperature rises.

A measurement that allows us to compare how well the water, or any material, is absorbing incident radiation of different frequencies is the **absorption coefficient**. This tells us what proportion of the radiation penetrates to any depth of the material. The more absorbing the material, the lower the proportion of radiation that will reach any given depth and the higher the value of the absorption coefficient. This band of absorption is broad, stretching from about 1 MHz, at which the coefficient is fairly small, reaching a peak at about 17 GHz, and still showing appreciable absorption up to many tens of GHz.

So, when designing our microwave oven, we choose a low enough frequency (2.5 GHz) where the radiation penetrates deep into the food, but at which there is still enough energy absorbed to heat the food. Higher frequencies would be more strongly absorbed, but the penetration is not so high so only the very outer surface of the food would be heated.

 If radiation of 17 GHz is absorbed by pure water at 20°C, what part of the water heats up most quickly?

As the absorption coefficient is greatest at this frequency, the radiation is absorbed before it penetrates very far into the water. It is then the surface of the water that heats the most.

(*Note:* In the microwave oven all the surfaces are exposed equally to the radiation.)

Food, of course, is not pure water. As well as ionic salts, the water within food contains dissolved fats and proteins. Water molecules tend to arrange themselves around these molecules in layers in which the water molecules have relatively fixed positions – the same as they are arranged in ice.

In ice, and in these solid regions around dissolved molecules, the water molecules are prevented from rotating by hydrogen bonding. As a result they have an **absorption band** at much higher frequency. Additionally, the ions are prevented from moving by the solid matrix of water surrounding them. Ice, therefore, does not absorb the microwave radiation at such a high rate as liquid water, in other words it has a lower absorption coefficient, and the radiation penetrates more deeply. When food is being defrosted, only a small amount of heating takes place to begin with, and defrosting proceeds slowly. Once a small amount of ice has turned to water the heating rate increases, and the food defrosts more quickly.

Exploration 3.7   Perfect potatoes!

Apparatus:

◆ pan of water (about half full) ◆ frying pan containing cooking oil (to a depth of about 3 mm) ◆ oven ◆ microwave ◆ one large or two medium-sized old potatoes ◆ a good knife and a chopping board ◆ hand lens or microscope (optional)

Most people prefer potato to be cooked and warm when they eat it. We usually cook it until the cell walls in the potato collapse and the potato becomes softer and is easily mashed with a fork. Exactly how we heat the potato makes a big difference to its texture and flavour, so in this investigation you can compare the heating methods, eat the products and consider the physics of a perfectly cooked potato. These instructions are written for a couple of students carrying out the investigation in a kitchen, but if you are working as a class, each pair of students could try one method – you could then investigate the effect of size, shape, time and/or cooking temperature on the nature of the cooked potato and report back to the whole class at the end of the session.

Set the oven at 200°C and put a pan of water on to boil. Wash the potato – don't peel it. Cut it into slices about 5–10 mm thick. Place one slice in the oven and one in the water. Note the time at which you do this. Turn the grill on full and place a slice of potato under the grill. Put the frying pan on a medium heat – keep an eye on it. When the pan is hot (but not smoking) put the potato into the oil and watch what happens. Try to heat the pan so that the potato is brown but not black after about 5 minutes. When it is brown on one side, turn it over to brown the other side. Check the potato under the grill – turn it over when you turn over the fried potato. Make a note of the appearance of all the potatoes after 5 minutes. When the second side of the fried potato is cooked, remove it from the pan. Also remove the other pieces of potato from the grill, the oven and the saucepan. Quickly cut or break them in half. If they are not soft inside return them for further cooking for 10 more minutes. Put a slice of potato on an ordinary (not metal) microwaveable plate. Put the potato in the microwave and turn on to full power for 3 minutes. Let the potato stand in the microwave for 1 minute more before removing it.

When the potatoes have been heated following the above instructions, examine their texture carefully – look at the inside of the potato, the skin and the cut sides of potato that were on the outside during cooking; use the hand lens or microscope if you have one. Make a careful note of the colour, the texture and, if you dare, the flavour of the potato. You may like to return the pieces of potato to be cooked further by the same method and study the effect of doubling the heating. Identify the main mechanism of heat flow in the cooking methods you employed. Relate this to the time it took for the potato to cook. Try to relate the texture of the potato to the way it has been heated.

Present your results as a summary table and/or a poster for food technologists that illustrates how the humble potato can be cooked to give different flavours and textures.

You may have realized that some of the changes in texture are due to the potato drying out. How do you think similar treatment of pieces of bread will change their texture? If you have time you could repeat the exploration using bread to test your predictions.

Achievements

After working through this section you should be able to:

- use the equation $\dfrac{Q}{t} = kA\dfrac{(T_1 - T_2)}{L}$ when energy is being transferred by conduction

- describe the behaviour of molecules involved in the conduction of energy

- interpret a phase diagram

- describe how average molecular energy relates to phase changes, including evaporation and vaporization

- give the effects of pressure on the boiling and melting points of different substances

- define heat capacity and specific heat capacity, and carry out calculations using these terms

- describe the behaviour of molecules involved in the convection of energy

- sketch intensity versus wavelength graphs for the radiation of energy from bodies at different temperatures

- use Wein's displacement law to find the wavelength of the radiation emitted from a black body using

$$\lambda_{max} = \frac{2.898 \times 10^{-3}\,\mathrm{m\,K}}{T}$$

- apply Stefan's law to find the power of the radiation emitted from a black body using

$P = \sigma AT^4$

Glossary

Absorption band   Portion of the electromagnetic spectrum that is absorbed by a substance

Absorption coefficient   The rate at which the intensity of electromagnetic energy falls off with distance through a substance.

Antinodes   Positions on a standing wave where the amplitude (largest displacement) is a maximum.

Black body   An ideal object that absorbs all the radiation that is incident upon it. It also emits radiation with a characteristic distribution corresponding to its temperature. The peak wavelength is given by Wien's displacement law.

Convection   As a volume of fluid is heated its particles gain kinetic energy and their average separation increases. The density of this volume of fluid therefore decreases and it rises through the rest of the fluid. It is replaced by denser, colder fluid, which in turn is heated. This produces a convection current and causes the fluid to be heated evenly.

Dipole moment   An object that has a neutral charge overall can have this charge spread unevenly so that some parts of it appear to be positively charged and others appear to be negatively charged. If this dipole is now placed in an electric field it will experience a turning force, or moment. Dipole moment is a vector quantity.

Evaporation   The process by which some particles that have enough energy leave a liquid and form a vapour even though the liquid is below its boiling point.

Free electrons Electrons that are only loosely held by nuclei and can move easily from orbiting one nuclei to another.

Heat capacity The ratio of the amount of energy transferred to an object to the temperature rise it produces. It is an attribute of the object, not of the material from which it is made. (See also *Specific heat capacity.*)

Infrared The band of wavelengths just beyond visible red in the electromagnetic spectrum. When infrared radiation lands on our skin it feels hot.

Le Chatelier's principle When a system is in equilibrium and something changes that would tend to destroy this equilibrium, then the system will adjust to oppose this change.

Magnetron An electronic device for generating microwave energy.

Microwave Electromagnetic radiation that is in the range of frequencies from 500 MHz to 1000 GHz.

Phase diagram A graph with temperature and pressure as its axes, showing the boundaries of the phases of a substance.

Resonant cavity A metal enclosure capable of maintaining a standing wave of electromagnetic energy.

Specific heat capacity The amount of energy required to raise the temperature of 1 kg of a substance by 1°C. It is an attribute of the material itself. (See also *Heat capacity.*)

Standing wave A wave that is confined and does not transfer energy from one place to another (propagate) as a moving (progressive) wave does. Energy that is added to the standing wave is stored in it. For microwaves in a microwave oven, energy is transferred from the standing wave to the food.

Stefan's law This gives the power of the energy radiated from a black body as $P = \sigma A T^4$, where σ is Stefan's constant ($\sigma = 5.67 \times 10^{-8}$ J s^{-1} m^{-2} K^4), A is surface area and T is temperature.

Thermal conduction The transfer of thermal energy through an object when it has a temperature difference across it.

Thermal conductivity The coefficient that determines the rate of thermal conduction for a given temperature difference.

Vacuum flask A vessel for insulating liquids from room temperature, consisting of a double-walled, evacuated and silvered, glass container. Also known as a Dewar flask and a Thermos flask.

Vapour A substance in a gaseous state below its boiling point.

Vapour pressure The pressure exerted by the vapour above a liquid when the liquid is below its boiling point.

Wein's displacement law The relationship between the wavelength of the peak of radiation from a black body to the temperature $\lambda_{\max} = \dfrac{2.898 \times 10^{-3}}{T}$.

Wiedemann–Franz law

$\dfrac{k}{s} = \text{constant} \times \text{temperature}$.

Answers to Ready to Study test

R1

$$\langle E \rangle = \frac{3}{2} kT$$

$$= \frac{3}{2} \times 1.4 \times 10^{-23} \, \text{J K}^{-1} \times 293 \, \text{K}$$

$$= 6.2 \times 10^{-21} \, \text{J}$$

(to two significant figures)

R2

Infrared.

Answers to questions in the text

Q1

At the higher temperature more water molecules have the energy to escape from liquid to gas. There are therefore more molecules striking and being cooled by the spoon. Condensation forms on it more quickly, but it also warms up more quickly too.

Q2

The wire gradually cuts through the ice, eventually falling out of the bottom. But the ice appears unchanged. In fact, you may be able to see the plane marking the path of the wire.

The ice below the wire is under pressure and the melting point lowers. The ice melts and the wire sinks to the ice below. Meanwhile the water above the wire is no longer under pressure and so its melting point returns to 0°C. It is cooler than this and refreezes.

Q3

$$C = \frac{Q}{\left(T_f - T_i\right)}$$

and

$$c = \frac{C}{m}$$

so

$$c = \frac{Q}{m\left(T_f - T_i\right)}$$

Q4

$$Q = mc\Delta T$$

so

$$\Delta T = \frac{Q}{mc}$$

$$= \frac{7500 \times 10^3 \, \text{J}}{60 \, \text{kg} \times 4190 \, \text{J kg}^{-1} \, \text{K}^{-1}}$$

$$= 30°\text{C (to two significant figures)}$$

Q5

$$Q = mc\Delta T$$

$$= 1.0 \, \text{kg} \times 442 \, \text{J kg}^{-1} \, \text{K}^{-1} \times (300 - 20)°\text{C}$$

$$= 442 \, \text{J K}^{-1} \times 280 \, \text{K}$$

$$= 123760 \, \text{J}$$

$$= 1.2 \times 10^5 \, \text{J (to two significant figures)}$$

The frying pan would have gained an additional 1.2×10^5 J through heating. The temperature throughout the pan will not be the same because energy is continuously transferred from the pan to its surroundings. Some is transferred to the air and carried away by convection and some is radiated to other objects in the room.

Q6

$0.8^{10} = 0.1$ to one significant figure, or approximately 10%.

Q7

$0.1^{10} = 1 \times 10^{-10}$ or 1×10^{-8}%.

Q8

(a)

$$\lambda_{max} = \frac{2.898 \times 10^{-3} \text{ mK}}{T}$$

$$= \frac{2.898 \times 10^{-3} \text{ mK}}{300 \text{ K}}$$

$$= 9.66 \times 10^{-6} \text{ m}$$

$$= 9.66 \, \mu\text{m (to three significant figures)}$$

(b)

$$\lambda_{max} = \frac{2.898 \times 10^{-3} \text{ mK}}{5800 \text{ K}}$$

$$= 5.00 \times 10^{-7} \text{ m}$$

$$= 500 \text{ nm (to three significant figures)}$$

Q9

$$\lambda_{max} = \frac{2.898 \times 10^{-3} \text{ mK}}{T}$$

so

$$T = \frac{2.898 \times 10^{-3} \text{ mK}}{\lambda_{max}}$$

$$= \frac{2.898 \times 10^{-3} \text{ mK}}{1.5 \times 10^{-6} \text{ m}}$$

$$= 1932 \text{ K}$$

$$= 1.9 \times 10^{3} \text{ K (to two significant figures)}$$

The peak is at 1.5 μm, but the short wavelength tail of the black body curve extends into the red end of the visible range. This is shown in Figure 3.9.

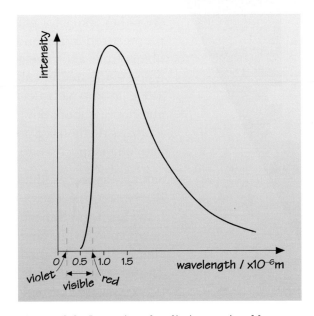

Figure 3.9 Intensity of radiation emitted by a black body at 1932 K

Q10

$$P = \sigma A T^{4}$$

$$P = 5.67 \times 10^{-8} \text{ J s}^{-1} \text{ m}^{-2} \text{ K}^{-4}$$

$$\times 1 \times 10^{-3} \text{ m}^{2} \times \left(1.9 \times 10^{3}\right)^{4}$$

$$= 0.1 \text{ kW (to one significant figure)}$$

The grill element will also lose energy through conduction to any other material with which it is in contact. The air surrounding the element will convect energy away from the grill as well. This means that the power that we have calculated for the radiated energy is too high.

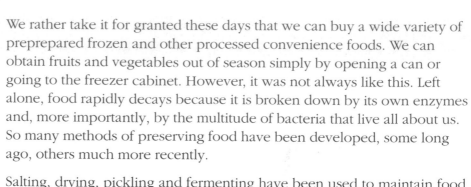

We rather take it for granted these days that we can buy a wide variety of preprepared frozen and other processed convenience foods. We can obtain fruits and vegetables out of season simply by opening a can or going to the freezer cabinet. However, it was not always like this. Left alone, food rapidly decays because it is broken down by its own enzymes and, more importantly, by the multitude of bacteria that live all about us. So many methods of preserving food have been developed, some long ago, others much more recently.

Salting, drying, pickling and fermenting have been used to maintain food reserves during lean periods for so long that we neither know when or how they were discovered. Freezing, chilling and canning are relative newcomers to our range of food preservation methods. Important social changes have accompanied the introduction of these new techniques. Those traditional methods of preservation would have been carried out at home, mostly for home consumption. But in the last 100 years a revolution in manufacturing and transport has meant that few of us now grow and rear our own food. Large-scale agriculture is the norm, and factory processed food is now transported from all over the world to large supermarkets for us to buy. The farmer and kitchen gardener, salting or drying their own food, have been replaced by the food and packaging technologists, microbiologists and chemical engineers. Manual labour has been replaced by powerful machines, wood and coal fires by electric heaters, old-fashioned recipes by carefully controlled processes. All of which rely on physics to some degree.

Foods can be found as solids and liquids, and gases can be important constituents of food and drink. Manipulating, storing and transporting food requires a thorough understanding of the properties common to each phase. In this section you will study some of this physics. You will learn about the three phases of water, and the relationship between their physical properties and the uses to which they are put. You will see how freezers and heat exchangers work, examine the effect that one optical property – refractive index – has upon the appearance of some substances, and take a look at how we can use this property to test foodstuffs in industry.

AT THE FACTORY

READY TO STUDY TEST

Before you begin this section you should be able to:

■ give basic descriptions of the three phases of matter: solid, liquid and gas

■ give the meanings of the terms 'frequency', 'wavelength', 'velocity' and 'speed'

■ draw a wavefront diagram to show the path of light through different transparent media undergoing refraction

■ sketch the passage of coloured light through a prism, and explain what is meant by the terms 'ultraviolet' and 'infrared'

■ calculate the average kinetic energy of gas molecules at different temperatures using $\langle E \rangle = \frac{3}{2}kT$

■ use heat capacity and specific heat capacity to calculate energy changes.

QUESTIONS

R1 (a) You have taken a frozen meal from the freezer and are defrosting it. What are the phases involved? At what temperature do you observe a phase change? (b) You heat water in a kettle. What phases are involved here? At what temperature do you observe phase changes? (c) White clouds are seen to emerge from the spout of the kettle. In what phase is this water?

R2 At the boiling point of water, what is (a) the average kinetic energy of the molecules in the steam just above the surface of the liquid (don't forget to use the boiling point of water on the absolute scale), and (b) the average speed of these molecules of steam, given that the mass of a water molecule is approximately 6×10^{-26} kg?

R3 Sketch a wavefront diagram to show ripples as they pass into water that is suddenly shallow.

R4 (a) Sketch a prism and draw the path of monochromatic light (light of a single colour) through it. (b) Why does light do this? (c) Show what happens to white light when it is refracted by the prism. (d) Why does this occur?

R5 There are two physical properties that have similar names – heat capacity and specific heat capacity. One of these is a property of a material and the other that of an object. (a) Which is which? (b) What units are they measured in? (c) Give the two equations showing how to calculate energy transfer using these properties.

4.1 Ice, water and steam

> Human beings were invented by water as a device for transporting itself from one place to another.
>
> (Tom Robbins, *Another Roadside Attraction*, 1971)

Food is essential for life, but so is water. We can survive many days without food, living only on our bodily reserves. But we cannot survive for long without water. We are at least 65% water.

Water is a major constituent of food. Its properties dominate the properties even of solid food.

Water also dominates the cooking process. Food cooks rapidly if we immerse it in boiling water. Steaming rather than boiling vegetables avoids losing many vitamins into the cooking water. Quickly driving water from food, as in deep frying, results in food that is crisp in texture.

Water is also essential to many processes that spoil food. Bacteria need water to live just as we do. Preservation of food by drying, freezing and salting makes this essential water unavailable and so stops bacteria thriving.

We meet materials, not only foods, in many forms and try to find ways to classify them. You will already be familiar with one convenient classification – into the three phases of solid, liquid and gas. Many foods, like water, melt or boil, i.e. change phase, so we need to understand the properties of each phase, regardless of the actual material, if we want to process, store or transport food.

Q1 Assign each property to one or more of the three phases.

1 Doesn't flow when a force is applied

2 Flows when a force is applied.

3 Regular geometrical structure.

4 Takes up the shape of its container, but without a change of volume.

5 Expands to fill its container.

6 Volume doesn't change much with temperature.

7 Volume is very temperature dependent.

8 Volume doesn't change much with pressure.

9 Volume is very pressure dependent. ◆

Solids have a definite shape, which they retain under most normal circumstances. Liquids have a fairly constant volume and, while they take the shape of the container into which they are poured, they have a level top surface. Gases have no definite shape or volume, but expand to fill any container into which they are introduced.

One of the factors that must be considered when foods are stored, sold or served is what container to put them in. The solutions are very different for foods in different phases.

Most of our observations of the behaviour of materials can be explained if we make the following assumptions:

- matter is composed of small particles (the particles are atoms if the material is a single element, molecules if it is a compound)

- these are continually in motion

- the energy of their motion can be increased by increasing the temperature of the material (or an increase in temperature is an external sign of increased energy of particle motion)

- changes in the phase of materials from solid to liquid to gas are caused by breaking the **bonds** holding particles together, through increased energy of their motion.

 ## Exploration 4.1   Modelling phases and bonds

Apparatus:

- ◆ Perspex box with sides of about 100 mm ◆ a few hundred 3 mm steel ball-bearings
- ◆ beaker of water

Pour the ball-bearings into the perspex box (as in Figure 4.1) and then add just enough water to wet them. This water tends to make the ball-bearings stick together and represents the forces, or bonds, between the particles of a real substance. If we are to break these bonds enough energy needs to be transferred to the particles. For these ball-bearings this **binding energy** is about 10 mJ. The repulsive forces between particles is represented here by the mechanical resistance of the ball-bearings.

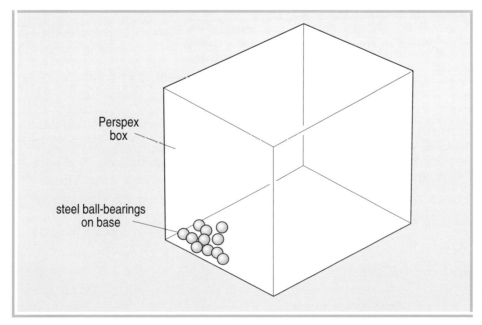

Figure 4.1
Steel ball model

If you tilt the box slightly all the ball-bearings will slide down to one side. Keep the box tilted like this and gently move it from side to side and back and forth. The ball-bearings settle into a regular pattern in which there is oscillation, but no ball-bearing moves out of its place.

Q2 Which phase are you representing here? ◆

(*Note:* The motion here is due to you moving the box and so is not the true internal oscillation that occurs in a real material.)

Figure 4.2(a) shows a representation of this phase.

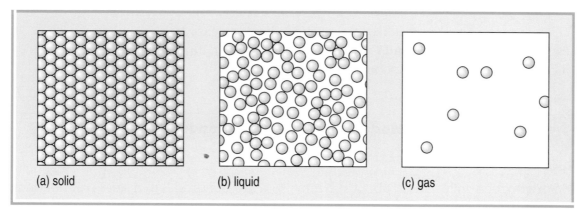

(a) solid   (b) liquid   (c) gas

Figure 4.2 Ball-bearings illustrating solid, liquid and gas

Gradually move the box more vigorously. You are increasing the average kinetic energy of the ball-bearings. This will lead to a pattern which on the whole is regular, but in which some of the ball-bearings have enough energy to break away and swap places with others. So, although most bonds are intact, enough energy is concentrated at some points within the system to overcome the adhesive forces of the water binding the ball-bearings together.

Q3 Which phase are you modelling here? ◆

Figure 4.2(b) shows a representation of this phase – you can see that a proportion of the bonds are broken.

Now continue by moving the box more vigorously still and remove the tilt so that it is level again, allowing the ball-bearings to move anywhere. When the ball-bearings have enough energy they will become completely detached from each other and will dart freely around the base. They collide with one another and with the box walls. The amount of energy that you have introduced into the system is greater than the sum of all binding energy of all the bonds.

Q4 What phase is this? ◆

Figure 4.2(c) shows a representation of this phase.

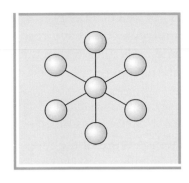

Figure 4.3 A ball-bearing and its six neighbours

In this two-dimensional model, each ball within the system is normally in contact with six others. It is bonded by water to six other balls, as shown in Figure 4.3, and for it to be removed from the system six water bonds must be broken. To break up the system entirely, that is, to change completely from the solid to the gas phase, all bonds between all balls must be broken. The total number of bonds to be broken is $3n$ where n is the total number of balls (3 rather than 6 because each of the six bonds is shared between two atoms). If the energy needed to break the bond between two adjacent balls is the binding energy, e, the total energy needed to break up the system is $3ne$. (This argument neglects the fact that balls at the surface of the system already have fewer than six bonds, but in an atomic system, the proportion of surface atoms to atoms in the body of the material is very small.)

In solids, the particles vibrate but, in general, they maintain their positions relative to other particles in the solid. There appears to be some permanent physical bond between each particle and its neighbours, otherwise solids would not have a permanent existence.

In liquids, there appears to be some movement of particles relative to one another, otherwise liquids would not flow. However, the fact that densities of liquids are usually only slightly less than the densities of corresponding solids suggests that, in liquids, the particles are still close enough together for most bonds to continue to exist, with a small number of particles at any time breaking away from their neighbours and reforming bonds with other neighbours to allow fluid flow.

Following this model, we can examine the difference between solids, liquids and gases by comparing average energies of the moving atoms with the binding energies of bonds between atoms or molecules.

 A system of atoms in any phase has a particular internal energy corresponding to one particular temperature. Write down the expression for this energy. (*Hint:* Start with the energy of one atom.)

The equation that gives us the average molecular kinetic energy is

$$\langle E \rangle = \frac{3}{2}kT$$

(You met this as Equation (2.2) on page 15.) If the number of molecules is n, then the total kinetic energy for the system is $\frac{3}{2}nkT$. This is the internal energy.

It is implicit in this expression that the distribution of kinetic energy within the system is unequal. At any time some molecules will have very little kinetic energy and some a great deal. So some molecules within the system have energies greater than the average internal energy per bond, while others have energies less than this average.

If the average kinetic energy $\langle E \rangle$ of the molecules in a system is much smaller than the binding energy, e, that is, if the temperature of the system is low, few bonds are broken. Very few molecules are able to escape, most remain close to one another in whatever structure has least potential energy. The actual structure depends on the arrangement of electrons within the atoms but, in general, it is a regular pattern resulting in a solid crystal.

If $\langle E \rangle$ is greater than the numerical value of e, then most of the bonds are broken and most atoms have enough energy to escape from their neighbours. The system must therefore be in the gas phase.

At an intermediate stage, when $\langle E \rangle$ is still less than the numerical value of e, the fact that the total energy is unequally distributed among the bonds means that in some regions there may be enough energy to allow the breaking of bonds to such an extent that atoms, or molecules, are able to move around and exchange places. This is the liquid phase, in which some bonds are broken, although most are not. Figure 4.2, showing a comparison of the ball-bearing model for the solid and liquid phases, indicates that, while in the solid model almost every ball is touching six others – it has six bonds – in the liquid phase the average number of bonds is less than six. **X-ray analysis** of liquids shows that the crystal structure still survives in this phase, and the fact that the amount of energy needed to change the solid to liquid is less than one-tenth that needed to change the liquid to gas suggests that, in a liquid, less than one-tenth of the bonds are broken. This is a state of dynamic equilibrium in which, although a definite proportion of bonds are broken, these are not always the same bonds. Rather, bonds between atoms or molecules are continually being broken and reformed with other atoms or molecules. Although fluid, liquids show many of the properties of solids, and may be considered to be much closer in form to solids than to gases.

Gases normally have a density of about one-thousandth that of solids or liquids. For example, the density of water in gas form at room temperature and pressure is about $0.8 \ \text{kg m}^{-3}$, while in liquid form at its boiling point its density is $1000 \ \text{kg m}^{-3}$. Because the mass of a gas is therefore about one thousand times less than the mass of an equal volume of its solid, there are about one thousand times fewer atoms in a gas than in an equal volume of the solid. The average interatomic separation r_g in gases must therefore be about $\sqrt[3]{1000} = 10$ times greater than in solids.

Solids normally have a density about 10% greater than the corresponding liquid.

If a solid has a density of 1100 kg m^{-3}, what would you expect the density of it to be when it had melted to a liquid?

Since a solid usually has about 110% of the density of its liquid form

$$\text{density of solid} = 1.1 \times \text{density of liquid}$$

$$\begin{aligned}\text{density of liquid} &= \frac{\text{density of solid}}{1.1}\\[4pt] &= \frac{1100\,\text{kg m}^{-3}}{1.1}\\[4pt] &= 1000\,\text{kg m}^{-3}\end{aligned}$$

Q5 In a sample of exactly 10 cm^3 of the above solid there are exactly 1×10^{20} atoms. The solid is heated and melts.

(a) What volume does the liquid occupy?

(b) How many atoms are there in 10 cm^3 of liquid?

Assume that the atoms take up a cubic space within the solid and the liquid.

(c) What volume is occupied by an atom of the solid?

(d) What is the length of the side of the cube occupied by one atom of the solid?

(e) What volume is occupied by an atom of the liquid?

(f) What is the length of the side of the cube occupied by one atom of liquid?

(g) What is the ratio of the length of the side of the cube occupied by an atom of liquid to that of the cube occupied by an atom of solid? ◆

The last value that you have just worked out is the average interatomic separation in liquids, r_1, and is about $\sqrt[3]{1.1} = 1.03$.

To summarize, in solids the atoms or molecules oscillate but maintain their average positions, while in gases they can move freely. In liquids, the intermediate phase, there is limited movement of atoms or molecules (or groups of atoms or molecules), and the crystal structure is largely maintained.

4.2 Frozen food

'It was cold last night. This meat is starting to freeze,' Deegie said, lashing a hindquarter to a packboard.

'That's good,' Tulie said, 'but there's more than we can carry. We will have to leave some.'

'Can't we build a cairn over it with the rocks from the fence?' Latie asked …

'We can, and we probably should, Latie. It's a good idea,' Tulie said, preparing a load for herself that was so huge Ayla wondered how even she, as strong as she was, could carry it. 'But we may not get back for it until spring, if the weather turns. If it was closer to the lodge, it would be better. Animals don't come around as much, and we could watch it, but out here in the open if something like a cave lion, or even a determined wolverine, really wants the meat, it will find a way to break in.'

'Can't we pour water over it to freeze it solid? That would keep animals out. It's hard to break into a frozen cairn even with picks and mattocks,' Deegie said.

'It would keep animals out, yes, but how do you keep the Sun out, Deegie?' Tornec asked. 'You can't be sure it will stay cold. It's too early in the season.'

(Jean Auel, *The Mammoth Hunters*, 1986, p. 145)

It is a mark of the success of freezing as a method of preserving food that we now hear criticisms that it is overused.

Freezing has become essential to modern food distribution, and allows the routine extension of a food's traditional season. It also offers us the opportunity to shift the burden of meal preparation on to manufacturers, allowing us to spend our time in other ways. Even some foods that we buy unfrozen may have at some stage been transported or stored frozen and then defrosted when the shop wishes to sell them.

The freezing of food was first carried out commercially in the 1840s, but it wasn't until the middle of the twentieth century, when domestic freezers became available, that the supply of frozen food became the major industry it is today.

Frozen food has many advantages, but freezing it in the first place is not without problems.

On very cold mornings in winter you may find that your milk has frozen in the bottle on the doorstep. Why has the milk expanded and pushed up the foil cap?

Milk is largely composed of water, which expands on freezing. Needing more space, it finds it easiest to expand through the top, pushing off the cap.

In ice, in order to maintain minimum potential energy, the molecules arrange themselves in a very open hexagonal network (as shown in Figure 4.4) so that the density of the solid ice is less than that of the liquid water. Water, unlike most materials, expands on freezing. This has a detrimental effect on some fruit and vegetables, such as strawberries and lettuce, because when they are frozen, the expansion of the water they contain disrupts their cell structure. When we defrost them later, the liquid from within the damaged cells is released, and we find a sad and soggy piece of food sitting in a pool of liquid, known in the food industry as 'drip'.

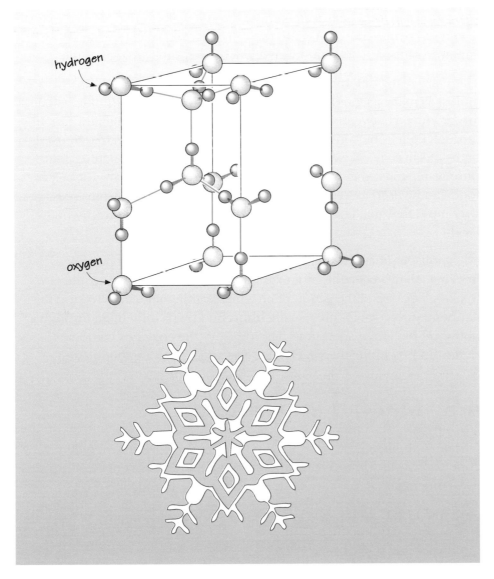

Figure 4.4
The crystal structure of ice

E ▸ **Exploration 4.2   Investigating rates of freezing**

Wear safety gloves
(thick insulating gloves)
and eye protection when
handling liquid nitrogen.

Apparatus:

- ◆ selection of food items to freeze ◆ access to a freezer
- ◆ flask of liquid nitrogen ◆ long tongs

Try freezing some different items of food at different rates. A fast rate can be achieved by plunging the item into liquid nitrogen (boiling point −196°C), or if this isn't available by placing small pieces directly on to the bottom of an ordinary freezer compartment with the control turned to the lowest temperature setting. A slow rate can be achieved by setting the freezer at a higher temperature (such that it takes all night to freeze). Your samples could include a piece of meat, a vegetable and soft fruit. Weigh each item before and after, and try collecting and weighing the 'drip' water. What conclusions can you draw as to the best way to freeze each food type.

How then can food be frozen without the cell walls being damaged? Small ice crystals cause less damage to the cell walls and so can preserve structure of food. These are formed when the food is frozen rapidly.

There are many different techniques used to freeze food in industry, almost as many as the different types of frozen food. Blocks of ice-cream are produced between two hollow plates which have refrigerant running through them. Chickens and other meat products are often frozen using baths of salt solution, which can be cooled to lower temperatures than pure water and remain liquid. Cold air, blown across a conveyor belt of food can be used to freeze inconveniently shaped items such as pies. For very rapid freezing, liquid nitrogen is sometimes sprayed directly on to food.

The spoilage process in many foods is not completely stopped by freezing. Many vegetables, for example, would still deteriorate after freezing because of the action of enzymes within their cells. To stop this happening, vegetables are usually **blanched** by passing them through a hot water bath for a short time. This destroys the enzymes without significantly cooking the vegetables. The vegetables are then frozen.

4.3 Melting and boiling

Our next problem is how to turn our frozen meal back into something appetizing again. Transferring energy into a body doesn't necessarily raise the temperature.

 What happens when you heat a block of ice that is at 0°C?

The energy transfer causes the block of ice to melt, but while it is melting both the solid and the liquid remain at 0°C.

Energy is required to change a solid into a liquid or a liquid into a gas (a change of state or phase): this is called **latent heat**. For example, 334 kJ of energy is required to completely melt 1 kg of ice at 0°C; 2256 kJ is required to turn 1 kg of water into steam at 100°C. These are called the **specific latent heat of fusion** and **specific latent heat of vaporization**, respectively. The word 'specific' indicates that we are considering the latent heat of 1 kg of a material.

We can explain latent heat in terms of molecular properties (i.e. using kinetic theory) just as we did for temperature. To melt ice we have to supply sufficient energy to break the weak bonds between some of the molecules. At the end of Section 4.1 we estimated the average separation of molecules in a gas and a liquid compared with a solid. In the solid ice, the molecules are moving about a fixed position, whereas in a liquid they have a much freer motion, although nowhere near as free as in a gas. In other words, as we melt ice and turn it into water, the potential energy of the molecules increases.

Q6 We have added energy to the system. Given that we have said there is no temperature rise, what has happened to the kinetic energy of the system? ◆

We might plot the temperature change of a quantity of water below freezing point as it is allowed to warm to room temperature, as shown in Figure 4.5. As time proceeds the temperature rises steadily. As the freezing point is reached its temperature finds a plateau; it does not change. Energy is still being transferred to the frozen water from its surroundings, however, and this is required to convert the ice into liquid water. Once the ice has melted the temperature begins to rise again. This energy is the latent heat of fusion.

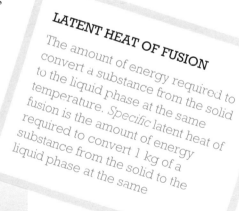

LATENT HEAT OF FUSION
The amount of energy required to convert a substance from the solid to the liquid phase at the same temperature. Specific latent heat of fusion is the amount of energy required to convert 1 kg of a substance from the solid to the liquid phase at the same

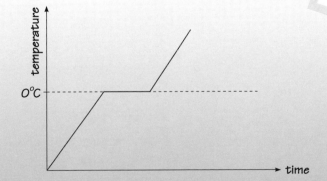

Figure 4.5 Temperature change in ice as it melts

If L_f is the (specific) latent heat of fusion for a material. How much energy is released when a mass m of that material freezes.

From the definition of latent heat of fusion, $Q = mL_f$.

Q7 (a) Given that, for water, L_f is 334 kJ kg^{-1} and the (specific) latent heat of vaporization, L_v, is 2256 kJ kg^{-1}, how much energy is required: (i) to melt 0.50 kg of ice to water at 0°C, (ii) to convert 2.5 kg of water to steam at the same temperature?

(b) If the steam now changes back to water and the water to ice, what energy changes do you expect? ◆

Exploration 4.3 shows you how to measure the specific latent heat of fusion of water.

Q8 A freezing machine in a factory is fed with ready-cut chips at a rate of 2 kg s^{-1}. Assuming the chips are at a temperature of 60°C (having just been through a blanching process), and that the chips end up frozen at 0°C, calculate the energy removed per second by the freezer. (Use $c = 4.2$ kJ kg^{-1} K^{-1}.) ◆

If we were to carry out a similar experiment to that shown in Figure 4.5, but with liquid water at boiling point instead of ice at melting point we would observe a similar phenomenon. The energy in this case is the latent heat of vaporization.

To find the energy, Q, needed to convert a mass, m, of water to steam use $Q = mL_v$, where L_v is the specific latent heat of vaporization.

LATENT HEAT OF VAPORIZATION
The amount of energy required to convert a substance from the liquid to the gas phase at the same temperature.

The low value of latent heat of fusion compared with latent heat of vaporization in metals (see Table 4.1) supports the theory that most bonds are broken on vaporization rather than on melting.

Table 4.1 Specific latent heats of fusion and vaporization

Substance	L_f/kJ kg^{-1}	L_v/MJ kg^{-1}
Oxygen	13.8	0.213
Nitrogen	25.5	0.201
Mercury	11.8	0.272
Water	334	2.26
Silver	88.3	2.34
Copper	134	5.07
Aluminium	395	10.8
Iron	275	6.29

Exploration 4.3
Measuring the specific latent heat of fusion of water

40 MINUTES

Apparatus:

- water ◆ calorimeter ◆ electric kettle ◆ thermometer ◆ ice ◆ kitchen towel
- balance

Place a known mass m_1 of warm water (a few degrees above room temperature) in a calorimeter and measure its temperature, T_1 (you can ignore the heat capacity of the calorimeter). Calculate the difference between T_1 and room temperature and call this ΔT. Take some pieces of ice, dry them on kitchen towel and immediately place them in the water. Continue until the water temperature is at ΔT below room temperature, T_2 (doing it this way means you don't have to apply a correction for energy lost to the air). Re-weigh the water to find m_2, the mass of the melted ice.

The energy lost by the water as it cools is

$$Q_1 = m_1 c_w \times (T_1 - T_2)$$

where c_w is the specific heat capacity of water. The energy needed to warm the melted ice from 0°C to T_2 is

$$Q_2 = m_2 c_w \times (T_2 - 0)$$

And finally the energy required to melt the ice is

$$Q_3 = m_2 \times L_f$$

Since

$$Q_1 = Q_2 + Q_3$$

you can see that

$$Q_1 - Q_2 = m_2 \times L_f$$

Substituting from the above equations and rearranging will give

$$L_f = \left[\frac{m_1 c_w \times (T_1 - T_2)}{m_2} \right] - c_w (T_2 - 0)$$

You can now insert the values obtained from your experiment to find L_f.

You should find a value for L_f of around 3.3×10^5 J kg^{-1} (to two significant figures).

When water is turned into steam, a lot more energy is needed to overcome the attractive forces between the molecules so that they can move around independently in the form of a gas. So the latent heat of vaporization, like latent heat of fusion, increases the potential energy of the molecules but not their kinetic energy, since there is no temperature change.

Q9 In one catastrophic practical session Kate knocks over a beaker of water at its boiling point. She moves quickly out of the way and only about 10 g touches the skin on her hand, which is at room temperature. Then Tom promptly scalds himself by leaning through the jet of steam, 10 g also at 100°C is in contact with the skin on his forearm. Calculate who will sustain the most severe burn. (Use $c = 4190 \, \text{J kg}^{-1} \, \text{K}^{-1}$ and $L_v = 2256 \, \text{J kg}^{-1}$.) ◆

Safety advisors tell us that water should never be poured on a burning fat fire. There is a good reason for this. When the water is poured on to the oil it sinks to the bottom of the pan because it is denser than the oil. However, burning oil will be at a temperature well above the boiling point of water, so the water is rapidly heated by the surrounding oil to above its boiling point, and therefore turns to steam. The pressure of the steam beneath the oil blows it out of the pan. This first explosion also breaks the flaming oil into small droplets. So instead of the oil burning only over the area of the pan, it now has a much larger surface area. The rate of burning therefore increases explosively.

40-50 MINUTES

Exploration 4.4 Measuring the specific latent heat of vaporization of water

Wear eye protection and follow your teacher's instructions when using a steam generator. Don't allow steam to contact your skin.

Apparatus:

◆ balance ◆ calorimeter ◆ steam generator ◆ thermometer

Set up the equipment as shown in Figure 4.6. Nearly fill a calorimeter with a known mass m_1 of water that is a few degrees below room temperature and measure its temperature, T_1. Calculate the difference between T_1 and room temperature and call this ΔT.

Put the tube from the steam generator into the water in the calorimeter so that steam passes through the water and heats it. Stop when the temperature is ΔT above room temperature, T_2. Re-weigh the water to find m_2, the mass of the condensed steam.

You should see dark rippling shadows on the bottom of the calorimeter. These are due to the **refractive index** of the hot streams of water being different from that of cold water.

 Why do we aim to have the start and finish temperatures equally spaced around the room temperature?

When the water is cooler than the surroundings, the surroundings warm the water. When the water is hotter than the surroundings the reverse is true. We are therefore trying to reduce the energy transfer between the water and the surroundings to improve the experiment.

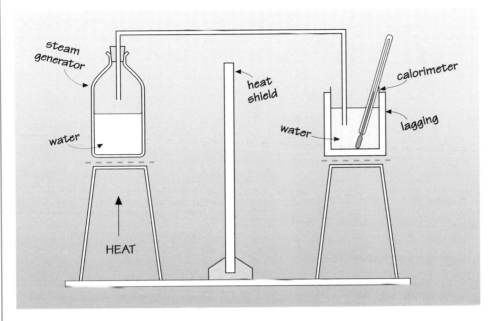

Figure 4.6
Equipment for finding the specific latent heat of vaporization of water

The energy received by the water as it warms is

$$Q_1 = m_1 c_w \times \left(T_2 - T_1\right)$$

where c_w is the specific heat capacity of water. The energy transferred as the condensed steam cools from 100°C to T_2 is

$$Q_2 = m_2 c_w \times \left(100°C - T_2\right)$$

The energy that is transferred as the steam condenses to water is

$$Q_3 = m_2 \times L_v$$

Since

$$Q_1 = Q_2 + Q_3$$

you can see that

$$Q_1 - Q_2 = m_2 \times L_v$$

Substituting from the above equations and rearranging will give

$$L_v = \left[\frac{m_1 c_w \times \left(T_2 - T_1\right)}{m_2}\right] - c_w\left(100°C - T_2\right)$$

You can now insert the values obtained from your experiment to find L_v.

So far we have considered a change of liquid to gas at the boiling point, but we know that a liquid does not have to boil to change to a gas. If a liquid is left to evaporate it will cool down. Why is this? The molecules in a liquid have a range of speeds, as shown in Figure 4.7.

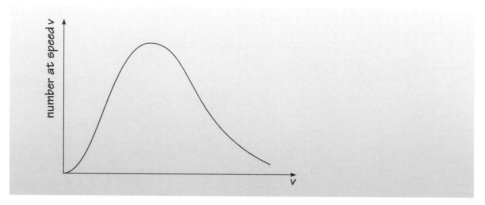

Figure 4.7 The distribution of speeds of molecules in a liquid

At any given temperature some molecules have a speed well above the average, and a few of these molecules have kinetic energies high enough to break the bonds that hold them in the liquid. If these very energetic molecules are close to the surface of the liquid, they can escape from the liquid and become water vapour. In water at 100°C, the average speed of molecules is about 720 m s^{-1}, and is sufficient to allow the molecules to escape. At any temperature below 100°C, only those molecules with speeds above about 720 m s^{-1} can escape; as the temperature is lowered, a smaller and smaller number of molecules have speeds above 720 m s^{-1}. So evaporation is slower at low temperatures.

At the normal temperature of the human body (37°C), water molecules must have kinetic energy well above the average to be capable of evaporation. If the molecules that leave have relatively high kinetic energy, the average kinetic energy of the remaining molecules will decrease; in other words, the water cools down.

We can increase the rate of evaporation of a liquid in four ways:

1 We can increase the temperature, which makes the molecules move faster and therefore enables more to escape.

2 We can increase the surface area, so that more molecules have a chance to escape.

3 We can blow air across the surface; this removes the molecules of vapour above the liquid and makes it easier for more molecules to escape.

4 We can reduce the pressure of the air above the liquid, which reduces the boiling point and the energy needed to escape.

Cooling by evaporation is a very effective mechanism used by some large mammals and birds to cope with high metabolic rates. When our surroundings are very hot, our bodies transport more water to the skin – we sweat. The evaporation of this sweat then cools us. If it gets cooler, we stop sweating!

Q10 Estimate the energy lost from the body per day by the evaporation of sweat, given that the average perspiration loss is 30 g per hour, and that the average latent heat of vaporization of perspiration at body temperature is 2436 kJ kg^{-1}. ◆

We can make use of the principle of cooling by evaporation. This was how the original coolbox worked.

> An old fashioned coolbox uses no energy, does not pollute and keeps dairy products quite satisfactorily. Ours measures $16^1/_2$" × $13^1/_2$" × $7^1/_2$" (42 cm × 34 cm × 19 cm) deep and consists of a glazed inside and porous exterior and solid top. A 2" (5 cm) trough around the top is filled with cold water and as it evaporates it reduces the temperature by about 10°C lower than the outside atmosphere.

(Letter in *Permaculture* magazine, no. 9, 1995)

 Exploration 4.5   Cooling through evaporation

Apparatus:

◆ 50 cm^3 measuring cylinder ◆ two Petri dishes
◆ clingfilm ◆ three thermometers ◆ balance

10 MINUTES setting up

Using the measuring cylinder, place 35 cm^3 of water in each of the two Petri dishes and then leave 35 cm^3 of water in the measuring cylinder. Put a thermometer in each of three containers and cover the measuring cylinder and one of the Petri dishes with clingfilm (see Figure 4.8).

Make a record of the temperatures measured over the following few hours and the change in mass (if any) of each of the containers.

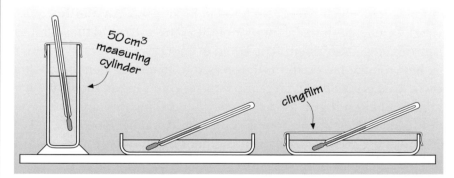

Figure 4.8 Set-up for Exploration 4.5

How do modern coolboxes differ from the traditional ones?

A modern coolbox relies on good insulation to keep things cool, rather than actively cooling them like the traditional one. In fact you could also use a modern coolbox to keep things warm.

A modern coolbox   A traditional coolbox

4.4 Freezers and heat exchangers

I don't want no ice man, I'm gonna get me a Frigidaire

(Popular song, 1941)

The industrialization of the freezing process began around the end of the last century, when efficient mechanical freezers became available, but domestic refrigerators are a relatively recent phenomenon. Up until the Second World War, small domestic refrigerators were very expensive, and in the USA the ice box was a cheaper alternative. This was simply an insulated box, which was partly filled with solid ice that was delivered to the home by the ice man.

Essentially the same cooling process is used in both domestic and industrial refrigerators, but, as we saw with the frozen chips, industrial freezers are on a much larger scale. They both make use of the latent heat of vaporization, which we encountered in Section 4.3. A **volatile** liquid is used to take energy from the interior of the refrigerator and transfer it to the surrounding atmosphere. The liquid evaporates easily into vapour; the latent heat required to do this is transferred from the refrigerator, cooling it down. An electrically driven pump removes the vapour and forces it into the **heat exchanger**, a set of pipes with cooling fins at the back of the refrigerator. Here the vapour is compressed and becomes a liquid again; the energy released as latent heat goes into the room. The cycle is then repeated. An adjustable **thermostat** switches the pump on and off, controlling the overall rate of evaporation and therefore the temperature in the refrigerator. (See Figure 4.9.)

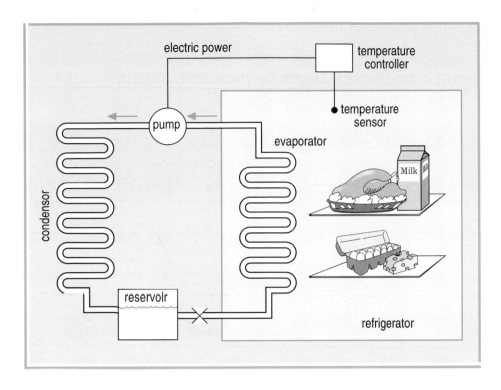

Figure 4.9
A refrigerator

As we said above, the refrigerator is driven by an electric pump. It is interesting to note that the electrical energy consumed by this pump can be a lot less than the amount of heat pumped by the refrigerator, often by a factor of two or three.

Q11 One day you get something out of the refrigerator and forget to close the door. Several hours later you come back into the kitchen. Assuming the kitchen is very well insulated, is the room at a higher or a lower temperature than when you left it earlier? ◆

There is one point we should make about refrigerators. You might assume that if you had a big enough refrigerator you could cool an object as much as you liked. What you would actually find would be that as the temperature became lower so the molecules of whatever you were cooling, say a cube of ice, would vibrate less and less.

You would also find that there is a temperature beyond which you cannot cool the ice any further. All the kinetic energy that can be linked with temperature has been removed from the water molecules. The temperature of the water is absolute zero and any energy still held by the molecules is known as **zero point energy**. Although we believe that absolute zero exists, we are also sure that it can never be reached. This is the **third law of thermodynamics**:

> The absolute zero of temperature can never be reached.

You are already familiar with the fact that a hot object will transfer energy to a cooler one, and we stated this more formally in Section 2.4 as the second law of thermodynamics. An example often found in the food

THIRD LAW OF THERMODYNAMICS
The absolute zero of temperature can never be reached.

industry is the heat exchanger, which is a system for transferring energy from one object to another.

Using a heat exchanger to pasteurize milk

In order to destroy the potentially harmful bacteria that it may contain, milk has to be pasteurized – heated to a temperature of about 70°C for 30 minutes, and then rapidly cooled before the flavour of the milk is significantly affected. This can be done on a large scale by using a heat exchanger (see Figure 4.10), in which the milk is passed through a system of plates or tubes in contact with hot water.

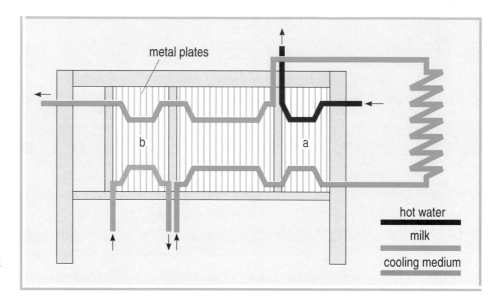

Figure 4.10
A heat exchanger. Milk is heated in region a and cooled in region b

A clipline plate heat exchanger

74

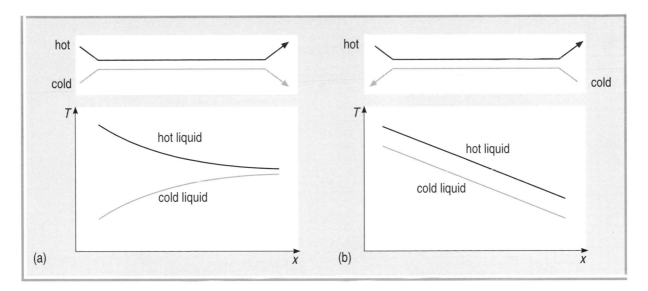

 It is usual for the hot water to flow in the opposite direction to the milk. Why is this?

If the water and milk were to flow in the same direction (**co-current flow**), their temperatures would change roughly as shown in Figure 4.11(a). The two liquids approach the same temperature. If the water and milk flow in opposite directions (**counter-current flow**), their temperatures would change roughly as shown in Figure 4.11(b). The colder liquid attains almost the temperature of the input hotter liquid by the time it leaves the heat exchanger. The hot liquid is cooled to nearly the temperature of the cold liquid by the time it leaves the heat exchanger.

Figure 4.11
How temperature varies with position in the heat exchanger with (a) co-current flow and (b) counter-current flow

4.5 Food drying processes

Many foods are dried in order to preserve them; for example, grapes, which we know in their dried form as raisins and sultanas, instant coffee, milk and egg powder, instant custard, gravy granules and herbs. Most grains (such as wheat, rice and barley) need to be dried on the farm after harvesting to remove residual water.

Remind yourself of the four ways that the rate of evaporation of a liquid can be increased from page 70.

The methods used are as varied as the products themselves. Traditionally many foods, including fruits such as grapes and dates, were laid in the sun to dry. More rapid methods are used nowadays, such as passing hot air over the food while it moves along a conveyor belt. Grains are typically dried in a cyclone drier (see Figure 4.12 overleaf). The particles are sprayed into the cylindrical section at the top and take a circular path around the walls. Warm air is injected from the conical section at the base. By the time the food reaches the bottom it will have been dried.

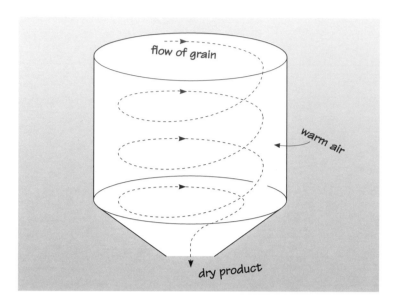

Figure 4.12
A cyclone grain drier

Milk is often dried by coating a heated roller with a thin layer of milk. As the roller revolves, the water evaporates out of the milk. The product is removed from the roller with a scraper.

Spray drying has been used for products such as instant coffee powder. The liquid coffee is sprayed into a chamber with a counter-current flow of hot air. As the liquid droplets are very small, they have a large surface area relative to their volume and so drying is rapid.

A modern innovation is **accelerated freeze drying**. The product is first frozen and then placed under vacuum. At low pressure the water evaporates from the solid without passing through the liquid stage, a process known as **sublimation**. Because the boiling point of water is decreased as the pressure is lowered, a point is reached where the water evaporates quickly even at room temperature.

In Figure 4.13 we have drawn a phase diagram to show how accelerated freeze drying works. Coffee is made at normal atmospheric pressure in hot water shown at point A. The coffee is then strained to leave only the liquid, which is then cooled. It follows the line A to B and crosses the line representing the freezing point for this pressure. Once frozen, the pressure can be reduced while the temperature is kept the same. This takes the frozen coffee from B to C, and on the way it crosses the sublimation point of water at this temperature. The frozen water turns straight to vapour, leaving only the coffee solids.

Path A–D shows how spray drying is carried out.

 Why use accelerated freeze drying instead of spray drying?

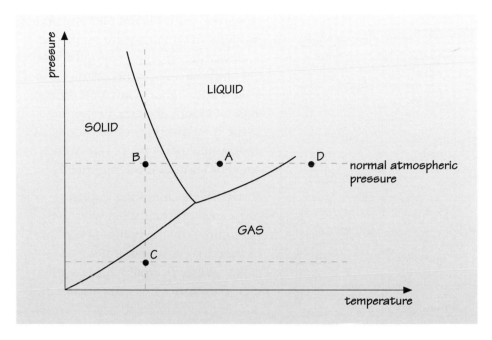

Figure 4.13
Using a phase diagram for water to illustrate the accelerated freeze drying of coffee

Spray drying involves heating the product. The flavours of many products, such as coffee and herbs, are damaged by heating. The use of accelerated freeze drying produces a dried product but through cooling rather than heating.

Q12 Look again at the drying methods outlined above. For each of them write down the physical process used to increase the evaporation rate, using the list on page 70. ◆

4.6 Why is milk white?

Why does a brown cow give white milk when it only eats green grass?

(Old pantomime song)

Ask any chef 'what is good food?', and you will probably be told about flavour, aroma, texture and appearance. Colour is an important aspect of a food's appearance because it tells us how fresh the food is and, from experience, how tasty it is likely to be (would you expect a green tomato to taste as pleasant as a red one?). Also, colour usually changes during cooking, so we can use colour to find out what stage the cooking has reached. Recipes often say something like 'cook until golden brown'. Manufacturers and retailers understand the use of colour when displaying and packaging food: products are photographed so that the colours look appetizing; artificial colours are added to processed food to improve the appearance; packages are designed to be eye-catching; supermarkets select their lighting very carefully to enhance their products, and so on.

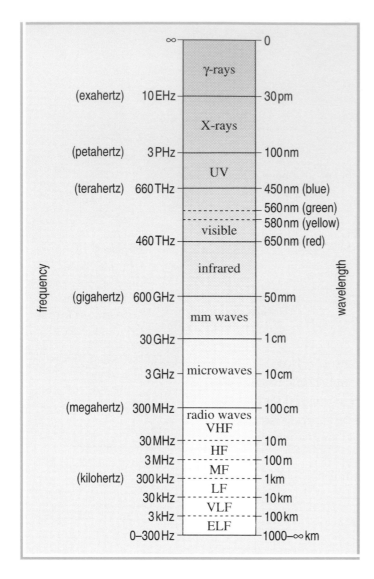

frequency		wavelength
∞	γ-rays	0
10 EHz (exahertz)		30 pm
	X-rays	
3 PHz (petahertz)		100 nm
660 THz (terahertz)	UV	450 nm (blue)
		560 nm (green)
	visible	580 nm (yellow)
460 THz		650 nm (red)
	infrared	
600 GHz (gigahertz)		50 mm
	mm waves	
30 GHz		1 cm
3 GHz	microwaves	10 cm
300 MHz (megahertz)	radio waves	100 cm
	VHF	
30 MHz	HF	10 m
3 MHz	MF	100 m
300 kHz (kilohertz)	LF	1 km
30 kHz	VLF	10 km
3 kHz	ELF	100 km
0–300 Hz		1000–∞ km

Figure 4.14
The electromagnetic spectrum

However, colour is not the only optical property in which we are interested. The way the surface of a food scatters light indicates its texture. Particles in a fluid scatter light (would you drink a glass of cloudy water?). Properties such as the refractive index are widely used as accurate measures of purity and concentration of food ingredients.

So what determines the optical properties of food? What we see is determined by the light reflected or emitted by a material. It is a characteristic of what happens when **electromagnetic waves**, matter and our brains interact and is an essential part of our everyday understanding of the world.

A knowledge of electromagnetic radiation is important for food scientists for other reasons too. When we grill or roast food, cooking is achieved by the absorption of electromagnetic radiation. The rate of absorption of radiated energy depends on the **wavelength** of the radiation, the intensity of the radiation field and the optical properties of the food. And the radiation does not have to be visible to cook the food – just as we can get sunburnt on a cloudy day, so food will cook with no *visible* source of energy. All electromagnetic waves carry energy.

What we collectively call electromagnetic waves – radio waves, microwaves, infrared, visible light, ultraviolet, X-rays – have no real boundaries between them. We have created the categories for our own convenience. The distinction of visible light is an obvious one since we can see it with our eyes. Infrared can be felt as warmth. Radio waves have been exploited in our communication systems. And so on. Figure 4.14 shows the electromagnetic **spectrum**

 Have a look around your kitchen. What sources of electromagnetic radiation can you find?

Light bulbs to illuminate the kitchen, LEDs in appliances, electric heating elements in grills, toasters or room heaters, microwave oven, even the room itself and its occupants are emitting radiation.

You will notice two scales plotted in Figure 4.14: **frequency** and wavelength. When we discuss waves we can describe them using either of these. So, a radio station might be said to have a frequency, f, of 200 kHz or a wavelength, λ, of 1500 m. The two quantities are related by the equation

$$v = f\lambda$$

Q13 In Question 8 in Section 3.5 you calculated the peak wavelength of the Sun's radiation using Wien's displacement law. The answer was 500 nm. From looking at Figure 4.14, what colour is this? ◆

In the nineteenth century, the Scottish physicist James Clerk Maxwell postulated that if electric and magnetic fields exist in free space then a changing electric field must be produced by a changing magnetic field and vice versa. He predicted the existence of electromagnetic waves, which move with a speed

$$v = \frac{1}{\sqrt{\varepsilon\mu}} \tag{4.1}$$

Where ε is called the **permittivity** of the medium in which the wave is travelling and μ is called the **permeability**. We use the values of ε and μ for free space (or a vacuum) as reference values. We denote these as ε_0 (the electric space constant) and μ_0 (the magnetic space constant) and their values are

$$\varepsilon_0 = 8.85 \times 10^{-12}\ \mathrm{F\,m^{-1}}\ (\textbf{farad}\ \text{per metre})$$

and

$$\mu_0 = 1.26 \times 10^{-6}\ \mathrm{H\,m^{-1}}\ (\textbf{henry}\ \text{per metre})$$

So, for light or radio waves travelling in a vacuum

$$c = \frac{1}{\sqrt{\varepsilon_0\mu_0}} \tag{4.2}$$

Q14 Using the values of ε_0 and μ_0 given above, calculate c using Equation (4.2). (*Note:* 1 farad = 1 $\mathrm{A^2\,s^4\,kg^{-1}\,m^{-2}}$ and 1 henry = 1 $\mathrm{kg\,m^2\,s^{-2}\,a^{-2}}$. These may look like odd units in which to express a velocity ($\mathrm{m\,s^{-1}}$), but the algebra does work out, as you will see when you answer the question.) ◆

When the wave is travelling through a medium such as glass or water, we must multiply these two values by factors known as the relative permeability, μ_r, and relative permittivity, ε_r (also known as dielectric constant), respectively:

$$v = \frac{1}{\sqrt{\varepsilon_0\varepsilon_r\mu_0\mu_r}} \tag{4.3}$$

(*Note:* ε_r and μ_r have no units.)

JAMES CLERK MAXWELL (1831–79)

James, it seems, was unhappy at school. He went to the Edinburgh Academy, but his clothes and his country accent made him stand out from the others, who gave him the nickname 'Dafty'. He was understandably shy. At 15 he invented the method of drawing an ellipse with string and two drawing pins. You may have tried this in maths lessons. Then, at 16, he left the Academy and started at Edinburgh University. At the age of 29 he entered Trinity College Cambridge and graduated as second wrangler, winning the Smith's prize. By the time that he was 35 he was professor at Marischal College in Aberdeen, where he married the Principal's daughter. Later he moved to King's College London, and then back to the family home in Scotland, where he did research while living as a gentleman farmer. He was persuaded when aged 43 to become the first Cavendish Professor of Experimental Physics in Cambridge and he set up the Cavendish laboratory. He died of cancer after a short illness, at the age of 48. He is remembered as the nineteenth century's most able theoretician.

James Maxwell worked mainly on electromagnetism, developing the fundamental equations that we know as Maxwell's equations. He showed that electromagnetic radiation can be considered to consist of two perpendicular oscillations, one electric and the other magnetic. He found that light only takes up part of the electromagnetic spectrum.

He also worked on colour theory, being the first to show that all colours can be made from mixing the three colours red, blue and green. He produced the first colour photograph using a three-colour process – it was of tartan. He also made extremely valuable contributions to the theory of gases and is remembered in the naming of the distribution of molecular velocities in a gas. He and Boltzmann worked on this independently and it is known as the Maxwell–Boltzmann distribution. Maxwell was an intuitive physicist who used maths effectively. He was not bogged down by dogma and preconceptions and he knew how to use his creative imagination.

(Source: Adapted from *Chambers Concise Dictionary of Scientists*, 1990)

For many substances we can take the relative permeability, μ_r, to be approximately 1. There are a few **ferromagnetic** materials with very high values. Iron has a μ_r of around 1000, and alloys containing iron, cobalt and nickel can have values up to 10 000. There is more variation between values of permittivity, e.g. air $\varepsilon_r = 1.0006$ (we usually write $\varepsilon_r \approx 1$), glass is typically $\varepsilon_r = 1.70$, polythene $\varepsilon_r = 2.3$, water $\varepsilon_r = 80$.

Q15 What is the velocity of light in glass? ◆

Quantum mechanics later revealed that we can also consider electromagnetic radiation to have the properties of moving particles (and the reverse is also true, particles can behave as waves). Figure 4.15 shows an impression of such a particle, called a **quantum** or **photon**, of electromagnetic radiation. The observer standing at a fixed point sees the wave travelling past at velocity v. The electric and magnetic fields at the front of the particle are small, building to a maximum and dying away again. This particle has energy. If it collides with an object this energy can be transferred. The amount of energy is proportional to the frequency, and therefore inversely proportional to the wavelength

$$E \propto f \quad \text{or} \quad E = hf \tag{4.4}$$

The constant of proportionality, h, is now known as Planck's constant, and has the value 6.626×10^{-34} J s.

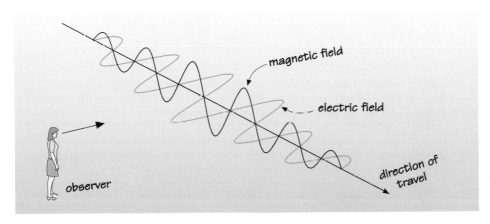

Figure 4.15
A quantum of electromagnetic radiation

What are the properties of all types of electromagnetic radiation?

■ They are manifested as an electric and a magnetic field perpendicular to each other, as shown in Figure 4.15.

■ The intensities of the fields vary with time and position in a sinusoidal waveform.

■ Their speed depends on the medium through which they are travelling. In free space they propagate with a speed of $c = 3.00 \times 10^8$ m s^{-1}.

■ Their frequency, f, wavelength, λ, and speed, v (or in free space, c), are connected by $v = f\lambda$ (or $c = f\lambda$).

■ A single photon (or quantum) of electromagnetic radiation has energy $E = hf$ ($h = 6.626 \times 10^{-34}$ J s).

Q16 What is the frequency of green light ($\lambda = 550$ nm)? ◆

Q17 What is the wavelength of a VHF radio station with a frequency of 90 MHz? ◆

Q18 What is the energy of a photon of blue light ($\lambda = 450$ nm)? ◆

Q19 What is the energy of a photon of far infrared ($\lambda = 10.0$ mm)? ◆

Q20 A grill emits radiation at a rate of 1 kW (1000 J s^{-1}). Assuming all the photons are emitted at a wavelength of 2.0 mm (this is not really the case as we will see later), how many photons are emitted per second? ◆

We have already said that the colours we see are the result of the interaction between electromagnetic radiation and the material of which an object is made. So what is milk made of? It is essentially an **emulsion** of small droplets of oil in water, stabilized by proteins and natural emulsifiers. Let us try to propose a model for the optical properties of milk, and see how closely it predicts our observations.

IS THERE A CASE FOR PERMITTING THE IRRADIATION OF FOOD?

Food can be irradiated by X-rays produced in an electrically powered X-ray tube or by the gamma-rays released from the decay of some **radioactive isotopes**. The main effect of this irradiation is to produce radicals that are generally very short-lived. These radicals damage the DNA of the micro-organisms living in and on the food and also the DNA in the food itself.

The micro-organisms are damaged in a way that stops them reproducing. In the food, processes such as sprouting and ripening that are triggered by enzymes are prevented.

The radicals produced affect the food in other ways as well. They oxidize fat and turn the food rancid. Various proteins and carbohydrates are also altered. However, these changes also occur in the normal storage and cooking of food. A test has therefore not yet been developed that can show if a food has been irradiated.

What are the best arguments for irradiating food? First, there are a few foods that are quite heavily contaminated with bacteria. Even when these are adequately processed they still cause a considerable number of people to suffer with gastro-intestinal upsets. Chicken, shrimps and prawns are the main foods in this group, but spices are also often heavily contaminated. Irradiating these foods would make a significant contribution to food hygiene.

Irradiating soft fruits extends their shelflife, although the argument for this is mainly commercial.

The public reaction to food irradiation has been almost uniformly hostile. Radioactivity has a very sinister connotation and there is a widespread assumption that the food is rendered radioactive. In fact, the induction of radioactivity by photons of up to 10 MeV (1.6×10^{-12} J) is extremely small and mostly of such short life that the levels at point of sale would be a minute fraction of the natural radioactivity in the food mainly due to the radioactive isotope **potassium-40** (also written as ^{40}K), let alone the total radioactivity in our environment.

(*Note:* Radioactivity is looked at more fully in the SLIPP unit *Physics in Space.*)

(Source: Adapted from Burgen, 1989)

Exploration 4.6 Looking at emulsions

Apparatus: ◆ glass beakers ◆ water ◆ oil ◆ milk ◆ bench lamp ◆ small elastic bands ◆ grease ◆ gaskets of various thicknesses, which can be cut from household rubber glove (ca. 200×10^{-6} m), sheet rubber used to waterproof babies' beds (ca. 250–500×10^{-6} m), polythene bag (ca. 50–100×10^{-6} m) ◆ pipette ◆ microscope ◆ slides and cover slips ◆ two test tubes and bung ◆ test-tube rack

(a) Pour some milk into one beaker, an equal amount of oil into another and an equal amount of water into a third. With the room darkened, shine the bench lamp on to these beakers. Holding a piece of white paper beside them, compare the reflected light from each beaker with that of the white paper. Now look at the light through each of the beakers in turn and comment on the transmission. Shine the light onto some clear writing and try to read it through each of these liquids in turn by holding them above the writing. Through which ones can you read the writing?

(b) Make up a set of at least three cells of different thickness to find out the thickest layer of milk through which you can still read some writing (Figure 4.16 shows you how to do this). How does this compare with the water and the oil?

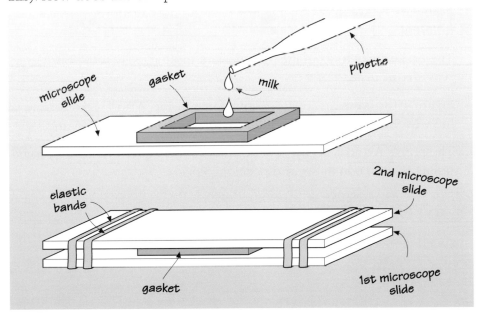

Figure 4.16 Making a cell. Place a gasket on a slide and add the milk (top), then cover with another slide and fix with elastic bands (bottom)

(c) In one test-tube, mix together water and oil in a 10:1 ratio. Push in the bung and shake hard until the oil is dispersed in small droplets through the water. In the other, pour an equal volume of milk. Now repeat the tests that you carried out in (a) and (b).

Put a drop of the oil/water mixture on to a slide and place a cover slip on the top. Make another slide with a drop of the milk. Compare these two slides under the microscope.

What happened to the optical properties of the oil and water when they were shaken together? How closely do the properties of this mixture match the properties of the milk?

You have seen that oil and water each transmit light with very little interruption. Milk, on the other hand, scatters light, and we can get the same effect by dispersing small droplets of oil in water. For us to form a clearer picture of what is happening we need to understand more about **refraction**.

In AD140, Ptolemy first investigated the refraction of light through glass, but was unable to propose a law of refraction that linked the angles of incidence and refraction. This was done by the Dutchman Snel in 1620 (his name is often also written as Snell). Snel found that the sines of these angles have a constant ratio for a given pair of transparent materials:

$$\frac{\sin i}{\sin r} = \text{constant}$$

Figure 4.17 shows a ray of light passing from one medium into another. The ray is refracted towards the normal. It strikes the surface at an angle of incidence, i, and passes through the surface with an angle of refraction, r.

Refraction occurs when electromagnetic energy travels across the boundary between two media in which the propagation velocities are different.

The easiest way to examine this constant more closely is to consider a **wavefront** instead of a ray.

Figure 4.18 shows a wavefront containing points A and C. Sometime later the wavefront has moved to the position containing points B and D.

The points A and C on the first position of the wavefront have become points B and D on its second position. Since

$$\text{speed} = \frac{\text{distance}}{\text{time}}$$

speed in medium 1, u, is given by

$$u = \frac{CD}{\Delta t} \tag{4.5}$$

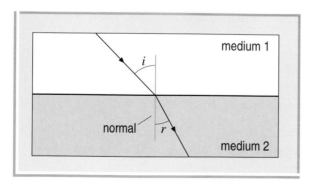

Figure 4.17 A ray of light passing from one medium into another

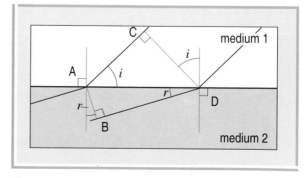

Figure 4.18 A moving wavefront

and speed in medium 2, v, is given by

$$v = \frac{AB}{\Delta t} \qquad (4.6)$$

The line AD is common to both triangles ACD and ABD so we can write

$$\sin i = \frac{CD}{AD}$$

and

$$\sin r = \frac{AB}{AD}$$

Substituting for CD and AB in Equations (4.5) and (4.6) we get

$$u = \frac{AD \sin i}{\Delta t}$$

and

$$v = \frac{AD \sin r}{\Delta t}$$

Combining these last two equations gives

$$\frac{u}{v} = \frac{\left(AD \sin i / \Delta t \right)}{\left(AD \sin r / \Delta t \right)}$$

$$= \frac{AD \sin i \times \Delta t}{\Delta t \times AD \sin r}$$

$$= \frac{\sin i}{\sin r}$$

So the relationship between the angles of incidence and refraction is determined by the speeds u and v in the two media. If we compare this equation with that summarizing Snel's discovery, we can see that his constant is actually the ratio of the two propagation speeds $\frac{u}{v}$.

From this we have formulated the concept of refractive index, where we assign each transparent material a number that we can use as a measure of how much the material refracts light. Look again at Figure 4.17. To find the refractive index of (for example) glass, we would make medium 1 a vacuum and place the glass as medium 2. The speed of light in a vacuum is c (3.00×10^8 m s^{-1}), so our last equation becomes

$$\frac{c}{v_g} = \frac{\sin i}{\sin r}$$

where v_g is the speed of light in glass, and we call this ratio the refractive index of glass, which we can write as n_g.

(*Note:* Making the subscripts the initial letter of the medium helps to avoid confusion.)

$$n_g = \frac{c}{v_g}$$

$$= \frac{\sin i_v}{\sin r_g}$$

If we replace the glass by water we can find its refractive index, n_w

$$n_w = \frac{c}{v_w}$$

$$= \frac{\sin i_v}{\sin r_w}$$

Since light travels fastest in a vacuum, the speed of light in any medium is less. This means that the lowest value of refractive index is 1. Some values of refractive index are given in Table 4.2.

Table 4.2 Refractive indexes of a few materials

Material	n
Air	1.000 292
Water	1.333
Ice	1.31
Ethanol	1.36
Polystyrene	1.59
Olive oil	1.46
Glass	1.5–1.7
Diamond	2.42
Zirconia (ZrO$_2$)	2.05
Rutile (TiO$_2$)	2.6–2.9

Q21 Given that the speed of light in a vacuum, c, is 299792458 m s^{-1} and using the values for refractive indices in Table 4.2, calculate the speed of light in: (a) air, (b) water, (c) glass $n = 1.6$, (d) diamond. ◆

Refractive index can be related to the relative permeability and permittivity of a material. Taking Equations (4.2) and (4.3), the speed of light in a vacuum (free space) is

$$c = \frac{1}{\sqrt{\varepsilon_0 \times \mu_0}}$$ (Equation 4.2)

and in a medium with a relative permittivity ε_r and permeability μ_r it is

$$v = \frac{1}{\sqrt{\varepsilon_0 \varepsilon_r \, \mu_0 \mu_r}}$$ (Equation 4.3)

The refractive index of a material is then

$$n = \frac{c}{v}$$

$$= \frac{\sqrt{\varepsilon_0 \varepsilon_r \, \mu_0 \mu_r}}{\sqrt{\varepsilon_0 \mu_0}}$$

$$= \sqrt{\varepsilon_r \mu_r}$$

but as for most media $\mu_r \approx 1$ then $n \approx \sqrt{\varepsilon_r}$.

In many situations we need to consider light passing from one material to another, say from water to glass. In this case the ratio of the sines of the angles becomes

$$\frac{v_w}{v_g} = \frac{\sin \theta_w}{\sin \theta_g}$$

We can take this further by looking at the equations for n_g and n_w above, which give

$$v_g = \frac{c}{n_g}$$

and

$$v_w = \frac{c}{n_w}$$

Combining these gives

$$\frac{v_w}{v_g} = \frac{c \times n_g}{n_w \times c}$$

$$= \frac{n_g}{n_w}$$

So we can now write

$$\frac{n_g}{n_w} = \frac{v_w}{v_g}$$

$$= \frac{\sin\theta_w}{\sin\theta_g}$$

To make this into a general equation we call the two media medium 1 and medium 2, with light passing from medium 1 to medium 2 and use values of refractive index rather than velocity. This equation now simplifies to

$$\frac{n_2}{n_1} = \frac{\sin\theta_1}{\sin\theta_2}$$

or

$$n_1 \sin\theta_1 = n_2 \sin\theta_2$$

Both of these variations are commonly used. For the first one we can also make the further abbreviation $n_{12} = \dfrac{n_2}{n_1}$, and this gives us a refractive index for any particular interface.

Q22 (a) Calculate n_{12} when medium 1 is water and medium 2 is glass. (b) Calculate n_{12} for light passing from glass to water. (Use $n_g = 1.6$.) ◆

Refractive index is normally quoted at a standard temperature, usually 20°C, and at a standard wavelength.

 You will have probably watched a beaker of water being heated with a Bunsen many times. If you have, you will have noticed dark rippling shadows in the water. What are these?

The refractive index of water is different at different temperatures. As convection currents are set up in the heated water light is refracted unevenly producing this shadowy effect. If you haven't noticed this look closely next time.

Q23 (a) Using data from Table 4.2, calculate the refractive index for a water–olive oil interface – n_{12}. (b) If the angle of incidence is 45° what is the value of the refraction angle? ◆

The geometry of a circle means that the angle of refraction of a ray passing into the oil drop is the same size as the angle of incidence of the ray on the surface of the oil drop as it leaves. See Figure 4.19.

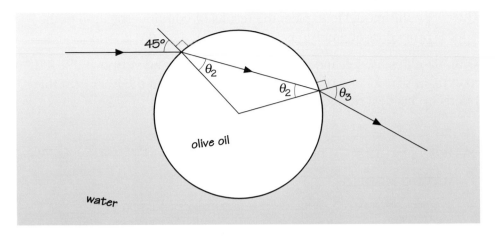

Figure 4.19
A path of a ray of light through an oil droplet

Q24 A light ray strikes the inside surface of the oil drop at the angle θ_2 that you calculated in Question 23. At what angle does the ray emerge from the oil drop? ◆

An oil drop is, of course, a sphere, so to gain a more accurate picture we need to imagine this happening in all three dimensions, not in just two.

We can now look again at the passage of light through an emulsion such as oil and water or milk. Figure 4.19 shows the path of one ray through an oil drop suspended in water, and Figure 4.20 shows a number of oil drops and rays of light.

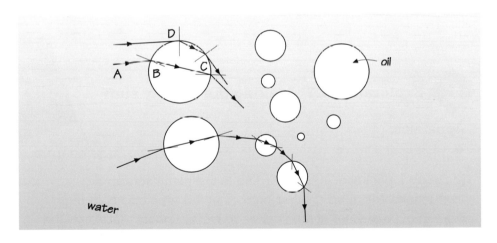

Figure 4.20
Refraction of light in oil droplets

 Is light that is parallel when it enters the emulsion still parallel when it emerges?

No, you can see that even if there was only one oil drop in the way each ray would leave the oil drop on a different path.

 Can this explain light being deflected back the way it came?

Yes, although one drop would not be able to do this, a ray being refracted through a succession of oil drops could produce this effect. Light can also be deflected at every other angle in this way.

Q25 Use this model to explain the results of your investigation of the optical properties of emulsions in Exploration 4.6. ◆

Q26 Use this model, and the values of refractive index from Table 4.2, to explain why a cube of ice may be transparent, but the hoar frost that builds up inside a refrigerator is not. ◆

MAKING MODELS

Science is not just about facts, but about understanding our surroundings. A key tool in this process is the development of models, whether for a small system of milk as we have just described, or for the entire Universe. Scientists begin with a model as simple as possible, and compare its predictions with what we accept as reality. Sometimes these predictions are good enough for the purpose for which they were developed. Sometimes more accuracy is required, and the model is then modified, extended, or scrapped altogether in favour of one that better explains the observed facts. This process can take years, or many lifetimes – or it may happen in brief flash of inspiration.

Many scientists are employed by industry, to collect facts and develop models to fit the needs of the process being researched. Sometimes scientists do it just for fun!

 Exploration 4.7   Making the wobbly stuff

15 MINUTES plus several hours waiting time

Apparatus:

◆ packet of jelly ◆ electric kettle ◆ milk ◆ two large beakers

Make up a packet of jelly according to the manufacturer's instructions. Make up another batch, but this time add cold milk instead of cold water at the final stage before setting. Observe the difference between the two.

4.7 Sugar solutions and perfect mirrors

 Exploration 4.8   The perfect mirror

Apparatus:

◆ ray box and low-voltage power supply   ◆ glass and perspex 'D' blocks

You need to carry out this exploration in a darkened room. The method of using the 'D' block is shown in Figure 4.21.

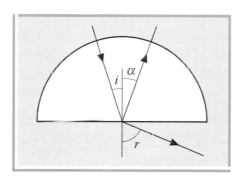

By aiming the incident light through the semicircular surface of the 'D' block to the centre of the flat side you ensure that there is no deviation at the curved surface. This will make taking measurements easier.

Start with an angle of incidence of 0° and gradually increase this to 90°. Look carefully at both the reflected and refracted rays. Note the changes that you see.

Figure 4.21   Using a 'D' block

One of the things that you should have noticed is this. At a certain angle of incidence the refracted ray seems to disappear and the reflected ray suddenly becomes bright.

At this and any larger angle of incidence all of the light is reflected and not refracted. Measure this angle for each of the 'D' blocks.

Now calculate the refractive index, n, of each of the 'D' blocks from several sets of measurements of i and r, using

$$n = \frac{\sin r}{\sin i}$$

 Comparing the equation that we have written here with the one for refractive index on page 84 this one looks as if the right hand side is upside down. Why is this?

For the equation on page 84, light was passing from the vacuum to the medium under test, here the light is passing in the other direction. This means angle i is on the same side as the medium under test instead of the other side.

We said earlier that to find the refractive index of a medium the other medium should be a vacuum. Here we are using air instead, is this a fair approximation?

Yes, $n_{air} = 1.000292$, which is approximately equal to $n_{vacuum} = 1$.

In Exploration 4.8 you have seen something that has found many applications, from binoculars to reflectors for vehicles; you may even have an example in your kitchen. The food industry certainly makes use of this phenomenon, as we shall describe. What you have seen is **total internal reflection**. When light is passing from one material to another with a lower refractive index there will be angles of incidence at which all of the light is reflected back into the first material and none is transmitted. The smallest value of i for which this occurs is called the **critical angle**, θ_c, and total internal reflection will result for any value of i equal to or greater than θ_c.

Figure 4.22 illustrates what you should have seen with three diagrams of increasing i. In (a) nearly all of the light is transmitted, with only a small proportion reflected. We often ignore the reflected ray when drawing these diagrams. When $r = 90°$ a dramatic change occurs. No light is refracted (enters the second medium), it is all reflected, as shown in (b). As i is increased further, shown in (c), all of the light continues to be reflected. For angles of i above θ_c we have the perfect mirror (as long as the surface is completely flat).

Since $n_1 \sin\theta_1 = n_2 \sin\theta_2$ we can also write out an equation for θ_c:

$$n_1 \sin\theta_c = n_2 \sin 90°$$

$$\sin\theta_c = \frac{n_2}{n_1}$$

Q27 Using values from Table 4.2, calculate the critical angles for the following interfaces: (a) water–air, (b) olive oil–water, (c) diamond–air. ◆

Figure 4.22
Variation of angle of refraction with angle of incidence for $n_1 > n_2$.

Many industries make use of total internal reflection to check on the composition of a variety of substances. In the food industry it is used to aid the control of processes in the preparation of, for example, soft and alcoholic drinks, dairy products, confectionery and flavours. A typical use

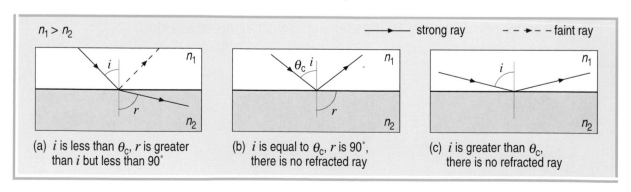

(a) i is less than θ_c, r is greater than i but less than 90°

(b) i is equal to θ_c, r is 90°, there is no refracted ray

(c) i is greater than θ_c, there is no refracted ray

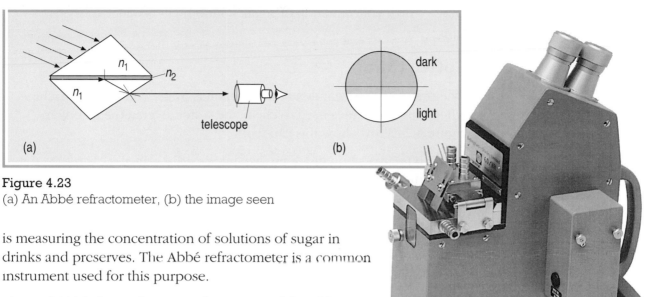

Figure 4.23
(a) An Abbé refractometer, (b) the image seen

An Abbé refractometer

is measuring the concentration of solutions of sugar in drinks and preserves. The Abbé refractometer is a common instrument used for this purpose.

Figure 4.23(a) shows the internal structure of the Abbé refractometer. The lower surface of the top prism is ground to a matte finish. The liquid to be measured is trapped in a thin layer between the two prisms. Light entering the instrument through the upper face of the top prism is scattered, over a wide range of angles, into the liquid captured between the prisms. The light leaving the second prism is observed with a telescope. Figure 4.23(b) shows the image seen through the Abbé refractometer, the field of view is divided into a bright and a dark field. The dividing line represents those rays in the liquid that are at the critical angle to the normal to the lower prism face.

The refractive index of the liquid will determine the critical angle for the interface between it and the lower prism. This in turn will determine the angle at which the boundary between the light and dark bands will be seen through the telescope.

The Abbé refractometer is ideal for indirectly measuring the concentration of sugar solution.

Table 4.3 shows values of refractive index for different concentrations of sugar solution.

Table 4.3 Refractive indexes for sugar (sucrose) solutions ($\lambda = 589.3$ nm, $T = 20°C$)

Concentration/%	Refractive index, n	Concentration/%	Refractive index, n
0	1.3330	50	1.4200
10	1.3479	60	1.4418
20	1.3639	70	1.4651
30	1.3811	80	1.4901
40	1.3997	85	1.5033

(Source: Chemical Rubber Company, *Handbook of Chemistry and Physics* (commonly known as the 'Rubber Book'), 1974, p. E224)

Q28 Which concentration of sugar solution will produce the largest θ_2? ◆

Coffee time

One use of refractive index in the kitchen is in the coffee filter machine, where it is sometimes used to check the water level in the reservoir. Figure 4.24 shows how this can work.

This is effective when the refractive index of the water, n_2, is higher than that of the plastic used, n_1.

 Why does it work when $n_2 > n_1$?

For total internal reflection to occur a ray of light must deviate away from the normal as it passes from medium 1 to medium 2. When $n_2 > n_1$ it is refracted towards the normal and so there is no angle of incidence for which light is totally internally reflected.

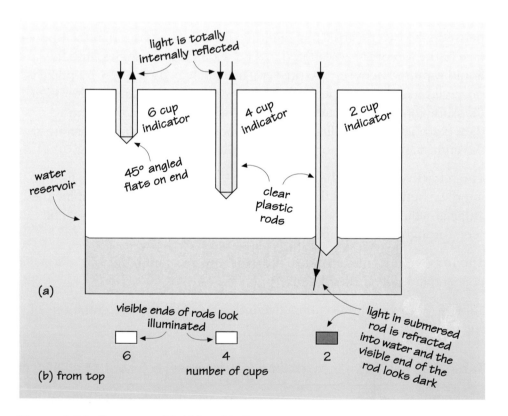

Figure 4.24 One type of fluid level indicator

Achievements

After working through this section you should be able to:

- describe the properties of the three phases of matter (solid, liquid and gas) in terms of the particles of which they are composed and the bonds between them

- explain how to calculate the energy required to break all the bonds in a solid from the binding energy

- say how the structure of ice affects its physical properties

- explain the concept of latent heat and use values of specific latent heat in the equation $Q = mL$

- describe how heat exchangers and refrigerators work and how they can be used in the food industry

- explain how the rate of evaporation of water can be increased in a number of different drying processes

- describe the nature of electromagnetic radiation with reference to its wavelength and frequency, use $v = f\lambda$ and state and use Snel's law ($n_1\sin\theta_1 = n_2\sin\theta_2$) and then the equations $v = \dfrac{1}{\sqrt{\varepsilon\mu}}$ and $c = \dfrac{1}{\sqrt{\varepsilon_0\mu_0}}$

- use the equation $E = hf$ and explain that it results from the belief that electromagnetic radiation can behave as particles

- explain how the refractive index of substances affects their appearance, and how it can be used to measure important properties of solutions.

Glossary

Accelerated freeze drying   An industrial drying process in which food is frozen, and the pressure then reduced until the water sublimes.

Binding energy   The energy required to separate completely atoms in a molecule or crystal.

Blanching   A very short period of cooking, usually in water, in order to destroy food spoilage enzymes.

Bonds   Forces that hold atoms together in molecules and crystals.

Co-current flow   The flow of two fluids in the same direction.

Counter-current flow   The flow of two fluids in opposite directions.

Critical angle   When a light ray crosses a boundary between media, the smallest angle of incidence, i, where the angle of refraction, r, is 90° is the critical angle, θ_c

$$\sin\theta_c = \frac{n_2}{n_1}$$

Electromagnetic waves   Waves propagating through space or a medium by the variation of electric and magnetic field intensity at right angles to each other, and to the direction of propagation.

Emulsion   A fine dispersion of one liquid throughout another.

Farad   This is the unit of capacitance, one farad is equal to one coulomb per volt. Capacitance determines the size of the charge that is induced between two conductors if there is a potential difference between them.

Ferromagnetic   A magnetic material that is magnetic because it contains iron.

Frequency   The number of times a periodic phenomenon occurs in a unit of time.

Heat exchanger   A system used to transfer heat from one fluid to another.

Henry   When a coil carries a changing current an emf is induced across the coil that tends to oppose the change. If the coil is designed so that this back emf is 1 volt when the current is changing at

1 amp per second, it has a self-inductance of 1 henry (1 H).

Latent heat   Heat energy transferred to or from a system to change its phase, without changing the temperature of the system.

Permeability   The ratio of the flux density produced in a material by a magnetizing field to the value of the field. It is represented by the symbol m and measured in H m^{-1}. When the material is a vacuum we call the value of m the permeability of free space (or the magnetic constant) and write it as m_0. $m_0 = 4p \times 10^{-7}$ H m^{-1}. The relative permeability of a material m_r, is a dimensionless constant used to scale the magnetic constant to the value of the permeability of the material.

Permittivity   The degree to which a material can resist the flow of charge. It is written as e and measured in F m^{-1}. When the material is a vacuum e is the permittivity of free space (or the electric constant), e_0. $e_0 = 8.9 \times 10^{-12}$ F m^{-1}. e_r is dimensionless and is the relative permeability of a material and is used to multiply the electric constant in the same way as relative permeability.

Photon   A quantum of light.

Potassium-40   An atom of potassium that has an atomic mass of 40. Potassium has 19 protons, and so this isotope has 21 neutrons, which makes it unstable and therefore radioactive.

Potential energy   Energy due to the position or arrangement of a body.

Quantum   A tiny discrete piece of electromagnetic radiation or matter. A description used in quantum mechanics.

Quantum mechanics   The theory of mechanics that describes the behaviour of photons of electromagnetic radiation as well as other objects.

Radioactive isotope   A form of an element that is radioactive. There may be other forms of the element that are not radioactive (stable). The difference between these isotopes is in the number of neutrons in their nuclei.

Refraction   The change of direction of the path followed by electromagnetic rays when passing from one medium to another, as a result of a difference in the speed of the waves in the two media.

Refractive index   For any medium, the ratio of the speed of light in a vacuum to the speed of light in that medium.

Specific latent heat of fusion   The amount of energy transferred when 1 kg of a substance is converted from solid to liquid phase (or vice versa) at constant temperature.

Specific latent heat of vaporization   The amount of energy transferred when 1 kg of a substance is converted from liquid to gas phase (or vice versa) at constant temperature.

Spectrum   A chart of intensity of emitted or absorbed electromagnetic energy, plotted against the wavelength, frequency or energy of the wave.

Sublimation   The process by which a solid evaporates without passing through a liquid phase.

Thermostat   A device for controlling the temperature of a system between two limits.

Third law of thermodynamics   The absolute zero of temperature can never be reached.

Total internal reflection   All light reflected at an interface where $n_1 > n_2$. No light is refracted.

Volatile   Evaporates easily.

Wavefront   The line that is made by the peak of a two-dimensional wave, e.g. a ripple on water. It is perpendicular to the direction of the wave.

Wavelength   The distance between successive peaks of a periodic phenomenon.

X-ray analysis A technique by which atomic arrangements within a solid can be determined by the diffraction they cause to rays of X-radiation.

Zero point energy The vibrational energy of a material can be reduced to a certain point but no further, this is the zero point energy. See *Third law of thermodynamics*.

Answers to Ready to Study test

R1

(a) In the freezer the whole meal is solid, but as it warms up the different components of the meal return to their original states. The water and other liquids return to the liquid state; solids, such as bone, will remain solid. The phase change you see will occur at the melting point of the liquids, which will be at around 0°C.

(b) Water remains as liquid water right up to its boiling point (100°C for pure water) after which, if you continue to heat it, it becomes gas. As the temperature rises, however, a larger number of water molecules have the kinetic energy they need to leave the liquid and the amount of water vapour above the surface gradually increases as the water is heated.

(c) Gaseous water is invisible, so the clouds that you see from the spout of the kettle as it boils are actually water that has condensed into liquid droplets, mixed with invisible gaseous water. See Figure 4.25.

R2

(a)

$$\langle E \rangle = \frac{3}{2} \times 1.381 \times 10^{-22} \, \text{J K}^{-1} \times 373 \, \text{K}$$

$$= 7.7 \times 10^{-21} \, \text{J}$$

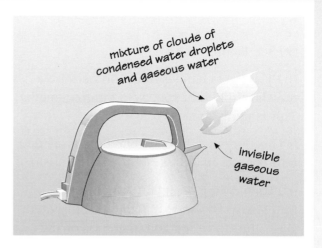

Figure 4.25 What comes out of the spout of a boiling kettle

(b)

$$\text{kinetic energy} = \frac{1}{2} m v^2$$

so

$$v = \sqrt{\left(\frac{2 \langle E \rangle}{m} \right)}$$

$$= \sqrt{\left(\frac{2 \times 7.7 \times 10^{-21} \, \text{J}}{6 \times 10^{-26} \, \text{kg}} \right)}$$

$$= 5 \times 10^2 \, \text{m s}^{-1} \text{ (to one significant figure)}$$

R3

Figure 4.26 shows a plan view of water waves passing into shallow water. You can see from the diagram that their wavelength and direction both change. This is due to their speed being less in shallow water. Refraction is caused by a change in speed.

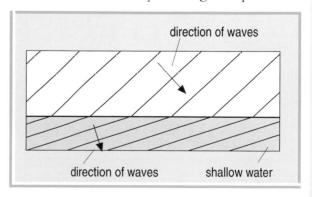

Figure 4.26 Water waves passing into shallow water

R4

(a) See Figure 4.27(a).

(b) The light changes direction because it travels at different speeds in different media. This is refraction.

(c) See Figure 4.27(b). White light is divided into colours as it passes through the prism.

(d) Each colour of light has a different frequency. The speed of an electromagnetic wave through a medium depends on the medium and on the frequency of the wave. Red light (low frequency) is refracted less than high-frequency violet light.

R5

(a) Heat capacity, C, is a property of a particular object; specific heat capacity, c, is a property of a material.

(b) Heat capacity is measured in $J\,K^{-1}$; specific heat capacity is measured in $J\,kg^{-1}\,K^{-1}$.

(c) $Q = C\Delta T$ and $Q = mc\Delta T$

Answers to questions in the text

Q1

Solid: 1, 3, 6, 8. Liquid: 2, 4, 6, 8. Gas: 5, 7, 9.

Q2

This is a model of the solid phase.

Q3

This is a model of the liquid phase.

Q4

This is a model of the gas phase.

Q5

(a) The density of the liquid is $1000\ kg\ m^{-3}$.

$$\text{density}, \rho = \frac{\text{mass}, m}{\text{volume}, V}$$

so, if m_s is the mass of the solid, and m_l the mass of the liquid

$$m_s = \rho_s \times V_s$$
$$= m_l$$

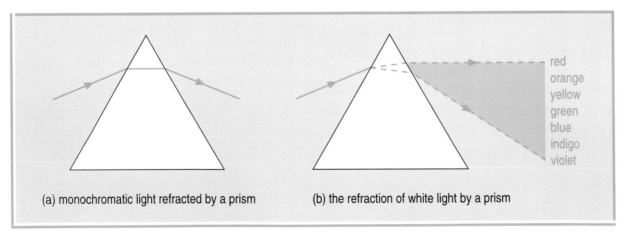

(a) monochromatic light refracted by a prism   (b) the refraction of white light by a prism

red
orange
yellow
green
blue
indigo
violet

Figure 4.27 (a) The path of monochromatic light through a prism, (b) the path of white light through a prism

$$V_l = \frac{m_l}{\rho_l}$$

$$= \frac{m_s}{\rho_l}$$

$$= \frac{\rho_s \times V_s}{\rho_l}$$

$$= \frac{1100\,\mathrm{kg\,m^{-3}} \times 10 \times 10^{-6}\,\mathrm{m^{-3}}}{1000\,\mathrm{kg\,m^{-3}}}$$

$$= 11 \times 10^{-6}\,\mathrm{m^{-3}}$$

$$= 11\,\mathrm{cm^3} \text{ (to two significant figures)}$$

(b) There must be

$\frac{10}{11} \times 1 \times 10^{20}$ atoms = 9×10^{19} atoms.

(c) In 10 cm^3 of solid there are 1×10^{20} atoms

so each atom occupies $\frac{10 \times 10^{-6}}{1 \times 10^{20}}$ m^3 or

1×10^{-25} m^3.

(d) The length of the side of the cube that contains this volume is l_s

$$l_s^3 = 1 \times 10^{-25}\,\mathrm{m^3}$$

so

$$l_s = \sqrt[3]{1 \times 10^{-25}\,\mathrm{m^3}}$$

$$= \sqrt[3]{100 \times 10^{-27}\,\mathrm{m^3}}$$

$$= 4.64 \times 10^{-9}\,\mathrm{m^3} \text{ (to three significant figures)}$$

(e) As there are $\frac{10}{11} \times 1 \times 10^{20}$ atoms in the

liquid, each atom must have $\frac{11}{10} = 1.1$ times

the space of an atom in the solid phase. So each atom in the liquid occupies 1.1×10^{-25} m^3.

(f) The length of side of cube that contains this volume is given by

$$l_l = \sqrt[3]{110 \times 10^{-27}\,\mathrm{m^3}}$$

$$= 4.79 \times 10^{-9}\,\mathrm{m^3}$$

(to three significant figures)

(g) the ratio

$$\frac{\text{length of side of cube occupied by atom of liquid}}{\text{length of side of cube occupied by atom of solid}}$$

is accurately given by

$$\sqrt[3]{\frac{\text{volume of one atom of liquid}}{\text{volume of one atom of solid}}}$$

and this is

$$\sqrt[3]{\frac{11/10 \times \text{volume of one atom of solid}}{\text{volume of one atom of solid}}}$$

$$= \sqrt[3]{1.1}$$

$$= 1.03 \text{ (to three significant figures)}$$

Q6

The average molecular kinetic energy of particles in a system is directly related to its temperature through the equation

$$\langle E \rangle = \frac{3}{2}kT$$

From this we know that a rise in temperature increases the average molecular kinetic energy, and that an increase in kinetic energy of the particles leads to a rise in temperature.

In this case we have transferred energy to the system but there has been no rise in temperature. So, from our understanding of kinetic theory, there must be no increase in the average kinetic energy of the particles.

Q7

(a) (i)

$Q = mL_f$

$= 0.50\,\text{kg} \times 334\,\text{kJ}\,\text{kg}^{-1}$

$= 167\,\text{kJ}$

$= 1.7 \times 10^5$ J (to two significant figures)

(ii)

$Q = mL_v$

$= 2.5\,\text{kg} \times 2256\,\text{kJ}\,\text{kg}^{-1}$

$= 5640\,\text{kJ}$

$= 5.6 \times 10^6$ J (to two significant figures)

(b) If the steam is allowed to cool and change back to water then ice, the two energies calculated in (i) and (ii) are released to the surroundings.

Q8

To lower the chips to 0°C requires the removal of

$4.2\,\text{kJ}\,\text{kg}^{-1}\,\text{K}^{-1} \times 60\,\text{K} \times 2\,\text{kg}\,\text{s}^{-1} = 504\,\text{kJ}\,\text{s}^{-1}$

To freeze the chips requires the removal of

$330\,\text{kJ}\,\text{kg}^{-1} \times 2\,\text{kg}\,\text{s}^{-1} = 660\,\text{kJ}\,\text{s}^{-1}$

So the total energy removed is 1164 kJ s^{-1}, or approximately 1 MW.

Q9

Kate's 0.01 kg water cools from 100°C to 20°C at 4190 J kg^{-1} K^{-1}.

The energy released is calculated using

$Q = mc\Delta T$

$= 0.01\,\text{kg} \times 4190\,\text{J}\,\text{kg}^{-1}\,\text{K}^{-1} \times 80\,\text{K}$

$= 3.4\,\text{kJ}$

Tom's 0.01 kg of steam released energy as it condensed at 100°C. This is calculated using

$Q = mL_v$

$= 0.01\,\text{kg} \times 2256\,\text{kJ}\,\text{kg}^{-1}$

$= 23\,\text{kJ}$

After the steam has condensed, the liquid water releases the same energy as Kate's water, so Tom receives in total

23 kJ + 3.4 kJ = 26 kJ

almost eight times as much as Kate. Steam is much more dangerous than boiling water.

Q10

$Q = mL_v$

so

energy removed from the body each hour

$= 30 \times 10^{-3}\,\text{kg} \times 2436 \times 10^3\,\text{J}\,\text{kg}^{-1}$

$= 73080\,\text{J}$

and over 24 hours the energy removed is 73 080 J × 24 h.

We therefore lose about 1.8 MJ per day through the evaporation of sweat.

Q11

Any energy emitted by the radiator at the back of the refrigerator is exactly equalled by that removed from the room by the cold surfaces. However, the room will be slightly warmer because the electric motor becomes warm through working and this energy is in turn transferred to the room.

Q12

1 *Increased temperature*: sundrying grapes and other fruit, conveyor belt drying with hot air; cyclone dryer; heated roller for milk and other liquids; spray drying.

2 *Increased surface area*: cyclone dryer; heated roller for milk and other liquids; spray drying.

3 *Fast moving air*: conveyor belt dryer, cyclone dryer.

4   *Reduced pressure of the air above the liquid or solid*: accelerated freeze drying.

Q13

500 nm is the wavelength of the colour blue.

Q14

$$c = \frac{1}{\sqrt{\varepsilon_0 \mu_0}}$$

$$= \frac{1}{\sqrt{\left(8.85 \times 10^{-12}\,\text{F m}^{-1}\right) \times \left(1.26 \times 10^{-6}\,\text{H m}^{-1}\right)}}$$

$$= \frac{1}{\sqrt{\left(8.85 \times 10^{-12}\,\text{A}^2\,\text{s}^4\,\text{kg}^{-1}\,\text{m}^{-3}\right) \times \left(1.26 \times 10^{-6}\,\text{kg m s}^{-2}\,\text{A}^{-2}\right)}}$$

$$= \frac{1}{\sqrt{1.1151 \times 10^{-17}\,\text{s}^2\,\text{m}^{-2}}}$$

$$= 2.995 \times 10^8\,\text{m s}^{-1}$$

$$= 3.00 \times 10^8\,\text{m s}^{-1}\ \text{(to three significant figures)}$$

Q15

$$c = \frac{1}{\sqrt{\varepsilon_0 \varepsilon_r\, \mu_0 \mu_r}}$$

$$= \frac{1}{\sqrt{\left(8.85 \times 10^{-12}\,\text{F m}^{-1} \times 1.70 \times 1.26 \times 10^{-6}\,\text{H m}^{-1} \times 1.00\right)}}$$

$$= 2.297 \times 10^8\,\text{m s}^{-1}$$

$$= 2.30 \times 10^8\,\text{m s}^{-1}\ \text{(to three significant figures)}$$

Q16

$$v = f\lambda$$

so

$$f = \frac{v}{\lambda}$$

$$= \frac{3.00 \times 10^8\,\text{m s}^{-1}}{550 \times 10^{-9}\,\text{m}}$$

$$= 5.46 \times 10^{14}\,\text{Hz}\ \text{(to three significant figures)}$$

Q17

$$\lambda = \frac{v}{f}$$

$$= \frac{3.00 \times 10^8\,\text{m s}^{-1}}{90 \times 10^6\,\text{s}^{-1}}$$

$$= 3.3\,\text{m}\ \text{(to three significant figures)}$$

Q18

$$E = hf$$

$$= \frac{hc}{\lambda}$$

$$= \frac{6.626 \times 10^{-34}\,\text{J s} \times 3.00 \times 10^8\,\text{m s}^{-1}}{450 \times 10^{-9}\,\text{m}}$$

$$= 4.42 \times 10^{-19}\,\text{J}\ \text{(to three significant figures)}$$

Q19

$$E = hf$$

$$= \frac{hc}{\lambda}$$

$$= \frac{6.626 \times 10^{-34}\,\text{J s} \times 3.00 \times 10^8\,\text{m s}^{-1}}{10.0 \times 10^{-3}\,\text{m}}$$

$$= 1.99 \times 10^{-23}\,\text{J}\ \text{(to three significant figures)}$$

Q20

The energy of a single photon is

$$E = hf$$

$$= \frac{hc}{\lambda}$$

Number of photons emitted per second

$$= \frac{\text{energy emitted per second}}{\text{energy of one photon}}$$

$$= \frac{1000\,\text{J}\,\text{s}^{-1}}{\left(\dfrac{6.626 \times 10^{-34}\,\text{J}\,\text{s} \times 3.00 \times 10^{8}\,\text{m}\,\text{s}^{-1}}{2.0 \times 10^{-3}\,\text{m}} \right)}$$

$$= \frac{1000\,\text{J}\,\text{s}^{-1}}{9.939 \times 10^{-34}\,\text{J}}$$

$$= 1.0 \times 10^{25}\,\text{s}^{-1} \text{ (to two significant figures)}$$

Q21

(a)

The speed of light in air

$$= \frac{c}{n_a}$$

$$= \frac{299\,792\,458\,\text{m}\,\text{s}^{-1}}{1.000\,292}$$

$$= 299\,704\,944\,\text{m}\,\text{s}^{-1}$$

$$= 2.997 \times 10^{8}\,\text{m}\,\text{s}^{-1}$$

(to four significant figures)

(b)

The speed of light in water

$$= \frac{c}{n_w}$$

$$= \frac{299\,792\,458\,\text{m}\,\text{s}^{-1}}{1.333}$$

$$= 2.249 \times 10^{8}\,\text{m}\,\text{s}^{-1}$$

(to four significant figures)

(c)

The speed of light in glass (with $n_g = 1.6$)

$$= \frac{299\,792\,458\,\text{m}\,\text{s}^{-1}}{1.6}$$

$$= 1.9 \times 10^{8}\,\text{m}\,\text{s}^{-1}$$

(to two significant figures)

(d)

The speed of light in diamond

$$= \frac{299\,792\,458\,\text{m}\,\text{s}^{-1}}{2.42}$$

$$= 1.24 \times 10^{8}\,\text{m}\,\text{s}^{-1}$$

(to three significant figures)

This, to a certain extent, explains why diamonds sparkle. Their refractive index is high so they refract light through large angles.

Q22

(a) Medium 1 is water, $n_w = 1.333$

medium 2 is glass, $n_g = 1.6$

$$n_{12} = \frac{n_2}{n_1}$$

$$= \frac{n_g}{n_w}$$

$$= \frac{1.6}{1.333}$$

$$= 1.2 \text{ (to two significant figures)}$$

(b) The glass and water are now reversed

$$n_{12} = \frac{n_2}{n_1}$$

$$= \frac{n_w}{n_g}$$

$$= \frac{1.333}{1.6}$$

$$= 0.83 \text{ (to two significant figures)}$$

Q23

(a)

$$n_{12} = \frac{n_2}{n_1}$$

$$= \frac{1.46}{1.333}$$

$$= 1.10 \text{ (to three significant figures)}$$

(b)

$$n_{12} = \frac{\sin\theta_1}{\sin\theta_2}$$

$$\sin\theta_2 = \frac{\sin\theta_1}{n_{12}}$$

$$\theta_2 = \sin^{-1}\left(\frac{\sin 45°}{1.10}\right)$$

$$= \sin^{-1}(0.643)$$

$$= 40° \text{ (to two significant figures)}$$

Q24

The ray leaving the drop has

$n_1 = 1.46$, $n_2 = 1.333$, so

$$n_{12} = \frac{1.33}{1.46}$$

$$= 0.913$$

Also

$$n_{12} = \frac{\sin\theta_1}{\sin\theta_2}$$

$$\sin\theta_2 = \frac{\sin\theta_1}{n_{12}}$$

$$\theta_2 = \sin^{-1}\left(\frac{\sin\theta_1}{n_{12}}\right)$$

$$= \sin^{-1}\left(\frac{\sin 40°}{0.913}\right)$$

$$= 45° \text{ (to two significant figures)}$$

Q25

Rays of light striking the interface between water and oil in the emulsions will be refracted. Because the oil droplets are small,

and there are a multitude of them, this refraction will occur many times. The light is therefore scattered in all directions, including back towards the observer. Any light passing through will have suffered many such refractions, so rays of light from any object will have become scrambled, and the image that they carried destroyed.

Q26

Light will be refracted at any interface. In ice, interfaces occur only between air and the ice, but as the cube consists of a number of crystals in close contact, refraction will happen only at the surfaces of the cube. With hoar frost, which is made of lots of small, randomly oriented crystals, the refraction will occur many times, in many directions, including back towards the observer.

Q27

(a) Water–air

$$\theta_c = \sin^{-1}\left(\frac{1.000}{1.333}\right)$$

$$= 49°$$

(b) Olive oil–water

$$\theta_c = \sin^{-1}\left(\frac{1.333}{1.46}\right)$$

$$= 66°$$

(c) Diamond–air

$$\theta_c = \sin^{-1}\left(\frac{1.000}{2.42}\right)$$

$$= 24°$$

Q28

For total internal reflection $n_1 > n_2$. The greater the difference between n_1 and n_2 the greater the refraction, and θ_c will be realized at a lower angle of incidence. So the highest θ_c for the data in Table 4.3 will be for the lowest value of n, which corresponds to a 0% sugar solution (in other words, water).

5

Energy costs money. Industrial companies exist to make money. So, while we may have our own views about the need to conserve our energy resources, for a manufacturer the saving of energy, by reducing the amount of energy used in a process, or reducing the weight of a packaged article, comes down to a matter of cost and profitability.

The suitability of a material for use in manufacture or construction depends mainly on three properties: stiffness, strength and weight. The moulded plastic of a bottle in the supermarket must be strong enough to retain its contents, which are applying an outward pressure to its walls, and it must not break when supporting a reasonable load. It must also have stiffness: a container that stretches so much that it sags to a shapeless form would be unacceptable. Fortunately for our bottle designers, high strength and high stiffness usually go together, and when these properties are found in a lightweight material, as in some plastics, we have a very useful packaging material.

Other material properties may also be important. A two-piece metal can must be strong and stiff, and have high thermal conductivity, so that it can support its own weight and allow its contents to be properly heated during the sterilization process. But, again, it must also be light, a property not necessarily belonging to strong, stiff materials like steel. One solution is to make a can out of aluminium, which, while mechanically weak, is light and is a good conductor. But all of these properties must be balanced against cost.

A technologist is not only interested in the mechanical properties of food packaging – health is also a vital factor to consider. For instance, milk cartons, which are formed from continuous sheets of plastic-coated card, must be sterilized by passing the unfolded sheets through a bath of hydrogen peroxide before they are formed into long tubes, filled with milk and then cut and formed into cartons.

In this section we look at the energy cost of transporting our food, and at the technology behind food packages such as metal cans, plastic bags and plastic containers.

READY TO STUDY TEST

Before you begin this section you should be able to:

- relate force and distance to work done
- give a description of the electromagnetic spectrum and the meanings of the terms 'frequency', 'wavelength' and 'wave velocity'
- state the law of reflection
- apply the law of conservation of energy
- calculate the energy transferred given the values of power and time
- calculate weight from mass and the acceleration due to gravity
- name the three primary colours of light and explain how they combine to give the secondary colours and white light
- find the energy of a photon of electromagnetic radiation given its frequency.

QUESTIONS

R1 A force of 20 N moves a mass of 50 kg through 8 m. How much work is done?

R2 (a) What is the sequence of colours in the visible spectrum?

(b) Identify the probable colour of light that has a wavelength of (i) 4.0×10^{-7} m, (ii) 7.0×10^{-7} m.

(c) Calculate the frequencies of these colours.

R3 A 2 litre electric kettle is rated at 1.5 kW and takes 3 minutes to boil. How much energy has been transferred?

R4 What is the weight of (a) 1 kg of sugar, (b) 150 g of butter, (c) 1.3 kg of carrots? (Use $g = 10$ m s^{-2}.)

R5 Which primary colours mix to give: (a) cyan light, (b) white light, (c) yellow light?

R6 What is the energy of a photon of light of frequency 6.0×10^{14} Hz? (Use $h = 6.6 \times 10^{-34}$ J s).

5.1 To and from the shop

 Exploration 5.1   Energy transfers

Work out the answers to Question 1 on your own, then read the quotations that follow it. In groups, discuss your reactions to the answers to Question 1 and the quotations.

Q1   A couple drive to the nearest supermarket (a round trip of 8 miles, which takes 10 minutes each way) and buy some mushroom soup (524 kJ), a pizza (1000 kJ) and a chocolate fudge cake (1000 kJ per slice). They warm the soup for 3 minutes and the pizza for 5 minutes in a 600 W microwave oven (which consumes 1.2 kW). They eat the soup and pizza, and each has a slice of the chocolate fudge cake.

(a) Estimate and compare the energy transfers involved in: (i) getting the meal and (ii) cooking it. (Assume that the average power generated by the car is 50 kW.)

(b) How much energy was available to them from the food? ◆

Compare the total value of the energy transfers in Question 1(a) with the answer to Question 1(b). Do you think that something needs to change?

Can you agree as a group

■   what needs to change

■   how this should change?

The energy transfers that you have just considered form just one small part of the total energy transfers involved in preparing and transporting food. They don't include all the energy consumed in getting the food to the supermarket in the first place: growing, transporting, processing, packaging, storage. The energy costs of all of these are very variable.

> One current estimate for the USA is that, although one farm worker can now produce the food needed by upwards of one thousand other people, every kcal of food energy consumed requires on average a total expenditure of 9 kcal (including the cost of an average 2000 kilometres of transport). The food systems of industrial countries now account for nearly 20% of their total energy use.
>
> (Open University, U205 *Health and Disease,* Book 3, page 177)

> The remarkable achievements of the celebrated Industrial Revolution are now beginning seriously to be questioned principally because the environment was not considered at the time. It was felt that the sky was so vast and clear that nothing could ever change its colour, our rivers so big and their water so plentiful that no amount of human activity could ever change their quality, and there were trees and natural forests so plentiful that we will never finish them. After all, they grow again. Today we should know better.
>
> (Victoria Chitepo, Minister of Natural Resources and Tourism, Government of Zimbabwe, World Commission on Environment and Development Opening Ceremony, Harare, 18 September 1986)

5.2 In the can

Life, you know, is rather like opening a tin of sardines. We are all of us looking for the key.

(Alan Bennett in *Beyond the Fringe*)

Packaging technologists have to consider many different things when deciding on suitable materials. Will the packaged item corrode certain materials? What temperature range will it be used over? For example, a plastic tray for an oven ready meal will be stored in the warehouse at −20°C, in the home freezer at between −20°C and −10°C, and during the cooking process will reach up to 200°C.

CANNED FOOD

Canning food using iron to make the cans was invented during the Napoleonic wars, around 1810. However, its chemical reaction with acidic foods made it less than satisfactory as a container. Tin plate (steel coated with tin) is now used, as this provides a non-toxic corrosion-resistant coating. Most steel cans have a layer of tin, less than 0.4 mm thick, on their surface. To prevent the tin leaching into the food the interior of the can is coated with a thin layer of lacquer.

Early cans were made in three pieces – two circular end pieces and the body, which was formed into an open cylinder from a piece of flat tin plate. These were then soldered or simply folded together. More recently, tin plate discs have been punched into the form of an open-ended can with no side seams and, after being filled, a single end is fixed on with a folded seam.

Tin plate is much stronger than most polymeric packaging (i.e. packaging made from material that consists of long chain molecules known as **polymers**), and allows high stacking in warehouses and during transportation. It is opaque and impermeable to liquids and gases, so protecting food from deterioration. Because of its high melting point and high thermal conductivity, food can be both cooked and sterilized in the can after sealing.

Filling and sealing the cans is a fully automated process. The cans will be fed on to a conveyor belt. Partially cooked contents,

for example beans, will be injected, hot, into the cans, and a lid placed on top. The can will be rotated while a tool turns the edge of the lid over to seal the can.

Cans are sterilized by heating to high temperatures, either in a batch process in which the cans are sealed into a pressure vessel and steam injected, or in a continuous process in which the cans pass on the conveyor belt through a region of high temperature. The length of time the cans spend in this region is set by the need to kill all the pathogenic bacteria in the cans. This depends on the temperature, the type of food and the species of bacteria. The cans are then cooled and labelled.

Tin plated steel cans can be recycled. Magnets are used to separate them from other refuse. The tin is removed electrolytically for refining and reuse, and the steel provides scrap metal.

Efforts are being made to make cans lighter and easier to open. An aluminium drinks can has a mass of about 10 g. The mass of a typical tin plate soup can is about 50 g. But both of these figures are being reduced as advances in technology make it possible for thinner material to be used for cans, while retaining the strength required to protect their contents. Although tin plate cans still require the use of metal-cutting can openers, parts of aluminium cans can be selectively weakened to allow more convenient opening by the use of ring pulls.

Technologists will also consider the forces acting on the package. For example, a bottle containing a still drink needs to retain only the forces due to the mass of liquid inside, while one containing a fizzy drink has to cope with the additional force due to the gas pressure.

How will the package be filled? How will the package be sterilized? What is the final weight of the packaged item? Aluminium has different properties from iron. It is lighter but weaker. When iron corrodes the resulting oxide layer is permeable to water and oxygen, and the corrosion can continue until all the iron has turned to rust. A clean surface of aluminium, on the other hand, rapidly forms a layer of aluminium oxide (the same material as sapphire), but this is an effective barrier and so although the layer is very thin it prevents further corrosion.

Aluminium foil, which has a thickness of less that 0.2 mm, can be tightly wrapped around foods such as stock cubes and chocolate bars, or it can be pressed to form trays in which food is placed and then covered by cardboard or transparent polymeric material for presentation. Aluminium's comparatively high cost makes it more suitable for packaging small relatively high value items.

It is possible to make a choice between iron, aluminium and polymeric materials on the basis of their physical properties.One test that can be easily carried out on metals is to see how much they change shape when a force is applied to them. This would affect the choice of material for canning and the thickness that a can wall would need to be.

 Exploration 5.2   How stretchy is a copper wire? **50** MINUTES

Apparatus:

♦ G-clamp ♦ spacer block pulley with clamp ♦ hanger and set of 1 kg masses ♦ reel of copper wire ♦ balance
♦ large protractor ♦ pointer for pulley
♦ C-cores (usually used for electromagnets)

Figure 5.1 shows the arrangement of the equipment. The distance between the G-clamp and the pulley will depend on the length of the bench and the diameter of copper wire available, but between 1 m and 2 m should provide satisfactory results.

> The C-cores should be placed over the materials before they are loaded to avoid whiplashing if the materials break. Wear eye protection and do not put your eye close to the wire when it is loaded. Place a cardboard box containing packing under the weights so that they fall safely if a break occurs.

You will need to mark the pulley when the wire has just enough tension in it to be straight: the hanger should provide this.

Collect a set of values of mass and total angle that the pulley has moved through and add them to a table like Table 5.1.

If the diameter of the pulley is D, taking into account the groove, and the angle through which it has turned is θ, then the extension, e, of the wire between the clamp and the

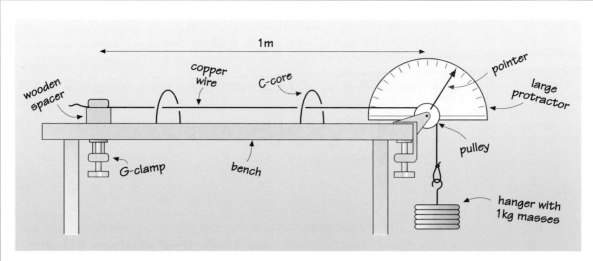

Figure 5.1 Measuring the extension of a copper wire

pulley is

e = distance that a point on the circumference has moved

$$= \frac{\theta}{360°} \times \text{circumference of circle}$$

$$= \frac{\theta \pi D}{360°}$$

Using this equation and $g = 9.81$ m s^{-2}, complete the remaining columns of Table 5.1.

Mass/kg	$\theta/°$	Tension/N	Extension/m

Table 5.1
Results for
Exploration 5.2

Plot a graph of the tension in the wire (y) against its extension (x). We would usually plot the variable that we are controlling on the x-axis and the variable that we are investigating as the y-axis. On this occasion the reverse is more convenient as we will later find the area under this slope. Most of this curve should be straight. Calculate the gradient of the straight part.

 Why calculate the gradient?

We would expect this to be a constant whenever we repeated this experiment with copper wire of this diameter and length.

Figure 5.2 shows an extension against force graph for a 0.25 mm diameter copper wire of length 2 m. Most metal wires show a similar, though not identical, curve, and numerical values differ from one wire to another.

 What can you say about the curve from O to A in Figure 5.2?

It is a straight line and it passes through the origin. This means that the tension in the wire is directly proportional to the extension, $F \propto e$. We can also write this as

$$F = ke \qquad (5.1)$$

where k, the **elastic constant** (or force constant), is specific to the piece of wire under consideration. Point A is the **limit of proportionality**. In region OB, if the force is removed, the wire returns along the line BO to its original length, and is said to be **elastic**. Point B is the material's **elastic limit**. If you think about this in terms of the atomic structure of the wire, you can say that when the interatomic forces are removed the atoms return to their original relative positions.

However, if larger forces are applied, and then removed in the region BC, the wire will again contract, but this time not back along the original graph, but along a line CE almost parallel to it, so that when all the force is removed, the wire has been permanently stretched. Some of the atoms now stay in the positions they were moved to during stretching. When the wire is stretched in such a way that part of the extension is permanent, such an extension is called **plastic**. As we saw above, such plastic deformation is important in the pressing and bending of metals to form shaped objects such as cans.

At D you can see that the curve turns back towards the extension axis. This means that once the extension has reached this point, even if you reduce the tension in the wire it can continue to stretch to breaking point.

Robert Hooke worked on many things, but he is most well known for formulating a law that we now know as **Hooke's law**:

As long as the limit of proportionality is not exceeded, the extension of a material is proportional to the force applied to it.

HOOKE'S LAW

As long as the limit of proportionality is not exceeded, the extension of a material is proportional to the force applied to it.

Equation (5.1), $F = ke$, is the mathematical expression of Hooke's law. However, its value refers only to the specific piece of wire under consideration. If we take a longer or fatter wire then we have to start all over again to find k. It is often useful to find the energy stored in a stretched wire or spring, and Hooke's law allows us to do that. We usually calculate the energy transferred, E, when a force, F, moves a distance, x, from $E = Fx$. We can say that energy is the area under the

Figure 5.2

Graph showing how extension changes with force for a 2 m copper wire of diameter 0.25 mm

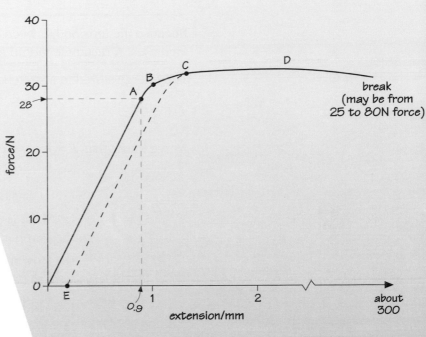

F versus *e* curve. Looking at Figure 5.3 overleaf we can see that this equation has to be modified in order to apply it here. A wire that has been extended a distance *x* and now has a tension *F* has a triangle under its curve. So if we use $E = Fx$ we calculate the rectangle marked, but the area under the line is half of this.

ROBERT HOOKE (1635–1703)

Robert Hooke was born on the Isle of Wight in 1635. At first he planned to join the church and went to Oxford as a chorister, but his poor health made him unsuitable for the church. He then turned to science and assisted Robert Boyle. He was considered an ingenious and expert mechanic. This mechanical skill led to improvements in the microscope, the telescope and the barometer.

Robert Hooke was one of the founders of the Royal Society and as Curator demonstrated three or four experiments at each weekly meeting. He became rich through his role as a Surveyor of London in the aftermath of the Great Fire of London.

In his 30s he realized that a spiral spring could control the balance-wheel on a timepiece, although Christiaan Huygens is known to have made the first model in 1674.

He had a reputation for being combative and had many disputes with Sir Isaac Newton, among others, mainly about who had thought of something first. He certainly felt that gravity followed an inverse square relationship, although Newton put the effort into developing this idea to its conclusion.

Hooke was not modest and laid claim to progress in several fields by publishing, when he was 41, *A decimate of the centesme of the inventions I intend to publish*. Among these was 'The true theory of elasticity or springiness' – under this heading was only the word 'ceiiinosssttuu', which turned out to be an anagram. People had to ponder this for another two years until Hooke published *De potentia restitutiva*, or 'of a spring', in which the anagram was revealed to be 'Ut tensio sic uis', which means 'As extension so the force'. Looking at the Latin you might guess that 'tensio' means tension, but it is actually Latin for extension.

He did much to benefit science and was very influential in making the Royal Society a professional body. It is recorded that he was respected, but also that he was too cynical and miserly to be much liked.

(Source: Adapted from *Chambers Concise Dictionary of Scientists, 1990*)

Why is the area below the line a triangle and not a rectangle?

Because the tension has been gradually increasing from 0 to *F* as *e* increases. A rectangle would need a constant force.

The energy stored in a stretched wire or spring is therefore

$$E = \frac{1}{2}Fx$$

As we know that $F = kx$ we can modify this to $E = \frac{1}{2}kx^2$

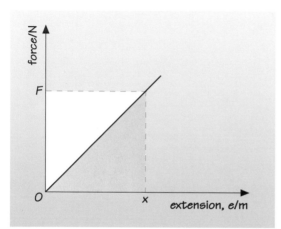

Figure 5.3
Sketch of $E = Fx$

Q2 Consider the wire in Figure 5.2.

(a) What is the force constant *k*, taking values on the graph at point A?

(b) How much energy is required to stretch the wire to its limit of proportionality? ◆

It would be much more useful to have a property that is characteristic of the material regardless of length or diameter. Much as pieces of copper of different volumes have different masses while copper as a material has an unique density (9000 kg m^{-3}), it is essential to have a form of elastic constant that relates to the material in general rather than a particular piece of it. Such a general property exists and is called the **Young modulus** (modulus just means number).

Thomas Young established the wave theory of light but here we are interested in his work on materials. He adapted Hooke's law to make it more generally applicable – by removing its dependence on length and cross-sectional area.

$$E = \frac{\text{stress}}{\text{strain}}$$

Where *E* is called the Young modulus, **stress** is the force per unit of cross-sectional area, and **strain** is the extension as a proportion of the original length. So if *L* is the original length of the material

$$\text{stress, } \sigma = \frac{\text{force, } F}{\text{cross-sectional area, } A}$$

and

$$\text{strain, } \varepsilon = \frac{e}{L}$$

Then we can write

$$E = \frac{\sigma}{\varepsilon}$$

$$= \frac{\left(F/A\right)}{\left(e/L\right)}$$

$$= \frac{FL}{eA}$$

(*Note:* The units of stress are N m^{-2} or Pascals (Pa). Strain has no units as both *e* and *L* are lengths and their units cancel out. The units of *E* are therefore N m^{-2}.)

In this way Young had incorporated both the cross-sectional area and the original length into his constant, giving a value that depended only on the material in question.

Q3 A 1.0 m length of copper wire A of cross-sectional area 0.50 mm^2 extends by 0.15 mm when a force of 10 N is applied to each end.

(a) What is its elastic constant?

(b) What is the extension of a 3.0 m length of copper wire B, of the same diameter, subjected to the same forces?

(c) What is its elastic constant?

(d) What is the extension of a 1.0 m length of copper wire C of cross-sectional area 2.0 mm^2, subjected to the same forces? (*Hint:* Think of this as four wires the same as A, with the forces divided between them.)

(e) What is its elastic constant?
For each of the wires A, B and C, calculate:

(f) The strain, or fractional increase in length, $\left(\dfrac{e}{L}\right)$, where *e* is the extension and *L* the original length.

(g) The stress, or force per unit area, applied to the ends of the wire, $\left(\dfrac{F}{A}\right)$.

(h) The Young modulus, *E*. This is the ratio of stress to strain in the relation:

$$\left(\frac{F}{A}\right) = E\left(\frac{e}{L}\right). \quad \blacklozenge$$

Place a cardboard box containing packing under the weights so that they fall safely if a break occurs.

 Exploration 5.3 Measuring the Young modulus

Apparatus:

◆ Young modulus equipment ◆ reel of wire ◆ mass hanger and a set of about ten 1 kg masses ◆ metre rule ◆ balance ◆ micrometer

The apparatus set up as shown in Figure 5.4 will allow you to make a more accurate measurement of extension than you could in Exploration 5.2.

 What features make this more accurate?

> The main scale is supplemented with a vernier scale allowing a measurement to one more significant figure. Also, attaching the main scale to a similar length of the same wire reduces any affects due to changes in the environment.

Set up the equipment making sure that the original length of the wire is no longer than you can measure with your metre rule. Make a note of the original length of the wire under test.

(*Note:* The wire does need to be under some tension just to make it taught enough to measure its original length. This will give you your first line of data in which the new length is equal to the old length and the strain will be zero.)

Make several measurements of the wire's diameter using the micrometer.

 Is it fair to find the diameter only at the start?

> This assumes that any change in diameter of the wire is negligible, and this is a fair assumption to make here. Test it by remeasuring the diameter of the wire when it has the greatest stress.

Make and record sets of measurements of the mass on the wire and its new length in a table like Table 5.2. Then complete the remaining columns in the table. (Use $g = 9.81$ m s^{-2}.)

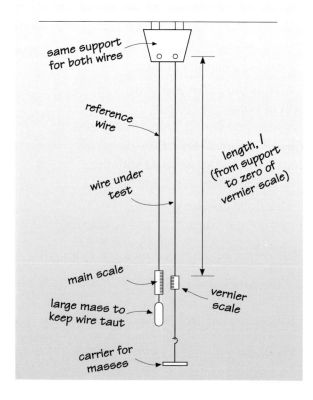

Figure 5.4 Equipment for measuring the Young modulus

(labels on figure) same support for both wires · reference wire · length, l (from support to zero of vernier scale) · wire under test · main scale · vernier scale · large mass to keep wire taut · carrier for masses

Table 5.2   Results for Exploration 5.3

Mass/kg	Length/m	Tension/N	Stress/Pa	Strain

Plot a graph of stress against strain and, by calculating the gradient of the straight line that you should be able to draw, determine E for the metal of your wire

 Remember your first line used a small tension in the wire when in reality the original length should have zero tension. How might this affect your results?

This could make all the strains lower than they should be. If this has happened you will notice when you come to draw the line of best fit. Your line will cross the stress axis above zero. The gradient will not be affected though

If a similar experiment to that in Exploration 5.2 is carried out with a glass thread, it is likely to break in the initial straight part of the graph. Materials like glass at room temperature, which break during elastic extension and do not reach plastic extension, are called **brittle**; those that experience plastic extension before breaking are called **ductile**. A metal container can be hammered out of shape – food cans are often dented without the seal of the can being compromised. In comparison, a glass jar would break completely with even a small knock.

 Glass jars are chosen as containers for foodstuffs in spite of their fragility. Why?

There are several reasons. Some foods are attractive when displayed in a transparent container. Jars are the traditional container for foods such as jams, so the public tends to expect them to be used. Also, food that is supplied in glass will often be kept for some time after opening, e.g. preserves, pickles, spices, and glass jars are easily resealed with a lid and will not taint the food in the way that some metals and plastics will.

If you would like to do some more work on elasticity, stress, strain and the Young modulus, refer to the SLIPP unit *Physics for Sport*.

5.3 In the bag

It has happened to all of us at one time or another. The trip to the supermarket has been reasonably successful. While we had to forgo the fresh salmon steaks, we did at least stock up on some essentials. We emerged, heavily laden, with a bulging plastic bag of shopping in each hand. Staggering up the road, feet and arms aching, we suddenly become aware that something is not quite right. The bag on the left doesn't look quite as it did when we packed it at the checkout. The normally white plastic between the letters is no longer white, but looking more and more transparent as the corner of a box of breakfast cereal forces its way through. As for the one on the right (the one containing all the cans of beans and tomato soup, with the eggs on top), its bottom seems to be getting nearer to the ground as the handles stretch. Something has to give, but which will it be? Will our knees collapse under the effort of carrying it all uphill? Or will the bag on the left split and spill its contents into the road. Will our aching fingers finally lose their feeble grip on the handle of the bag on the right. Or will the handle itself give way, the bag drop, and the eggs be ejected on to the pavement?

Plastic bags are often made from high-density polyethylene (often abbreviated as HDPE). This material, like other **organic polymers** (plastics), has a very large region in which it extends under load, gradually becoming weaker.

During the manufacture of the plastic bags, sheets of polythene are wound in rolls. This causes the molecular chains to align in the same direction, and increases the strength of the plastic in this direction. Manufacturers take this into account. They also try to reduce defects, such as patches of thin plastic and minor tears, to reduce the number of disasters like the one above.

5.4 There's sugar in my cardboard cereal packet

Yes, but we would recommend that your continue to eat the cereal and not the box! The sugar is glucose, which has molecules containing six carbon atoms. Fructose is another sugar whose molecules also have six carbon atoms. Table sugar is sucrose, which has 12 carbon atoms.

The cardboard in our cereal packets is made of fibres of cellulose, which is a polymer formed from long chains of glucose molecules. The cell walls of the fruit and vegetables that we eat also consist of cellulose, but, unlike some animals, we are not able to digest it. Cellophane, which is used a lot in food packaging, is also made of cellulose.

Exploration 5.4
Molecular alignment and the strength of plastic bags

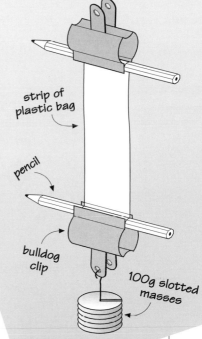

Apparatus:

◆ plastic bags ◆ long sharp scissors or scalpel and cutting board ◆ two bulldog clips ◆ two pencils ◆ retort or clamp stand ◆ 100 g hanger and set of 100 g masses

An arrangement for the equipment is shown in Figure 5.5. This is a destructive test so you will also need to make sure that the weights fall safely, perhaps by placing a cardboard box underneath them.

Cut several (ten is a good number) strips lengthwise from a bag and several from across the bag. Each strip should be the same width, say 3 cm, and long enough to give 10 cm of plastic between the pencils.

Figure 5.5
Equipment for testing plastic bags

 It is important to make clean cuts. Why?

Any nick along the edges will start a premature tear and will cause the piece of plastic to break early.

Now test each piece of plastic in turn. Load it gradually until it fails. Record all your results.

 After discarding any strips with visible damage should you take the average of your results?

Even after separating strips that are visibly damaged there may be some that have much smaller imperfections (possibly in the plastic itself) which still produce early failure. So, for this exploration it is best to find the maximum value that the strips in each direction can hold. You should find that the bags are stronger in one direction than the other and that the strongest direction should be vertical so that the bag can support its contents.

Manufacturers are interested in the total performance of their bags and would not only look at maximum values but also at the variation in their product.

Which plastic bags are the best?

Each supermarket has its own design of plastic bag. There are several differences between them – thickness, size, positioning of handle, shape and size of handle, colour. You should be able to design some suitable tests to compare a sample of bags. Discuss your findings with the other groups.

In sucrose the molecules stack together in a regular pattern as crystals. We have already looked at the crystal structure of solid water in Section 4.2. The chains of glucose in cardboard, however, are haphazardly organized, overlaying and running across each other. We call arrangements like this, where there is no regular pattern through the material, **amorphous** or non-crystalline.

 Which category would salt come under: **crystalline**, amorphous or polymeric?

Salt is a crystal; if you look closely you can see that it is cubic.

Plastics are often amorphous though some can crystallize. We would consider the polythene of plastic bags, where the molecules have an overall alignment, to be amorphous as this order has been mechanically imposed.

There is a lot of glass in a kitchen; this is amorphous – it is ordered only when you look at small groups of atoms. In fact, it resembles a liquid and can best be thought of as a solid liquid. Glass can crystallize over a very long time or when stressed.

5.5   In the yoghurt pot

The appearance of food and its packaging now plays a crucial role in consumer choice. In the highly competitive food industry, the extra sales a manufacturer might gain from having a more attractive product than its competitor can make all the difference between profit and loss. The next time that you are in a supermarket, look at the products on a section of shelving or in a chilled compartment – are any of the packages designed to draw the eye? Some companies have gone as far as placing hidden cameras among items in an effort to find out which are the most effective packages for drawing attention.

Whatever our objections might be to overpackaged food, as scientists we can appreciate that the appearance of a plastic package is due to the physical process of the interaction between light and the material of which the package is made.

Exploration 5.5 Colour in polystyrene cartons

Apparatus:

◆ clean polystyrene container with white sides and clear lid
◆ darkened room ◆ light source, such as a bench lamp

10 MINUTES

Test the white and clear polystyrene to see if light is transmitted through the plastic and reflected by it.

If the light is reflected, is it scattered? Is this due to the surface of the material or the material itself?

Cut the plastic and decide whether it is white just on the surface or all the way through.

Plastic manufacturers tailor their materials to suit the purpose. The clear plastic lid of a spread box is designed to show the contents clearly, or to show the printing on inner foil seals. The opaque tub is designed to minimize the amount of light penetrating the food. This reduces deterioration while on the supermarket shelf, and additionally provides a white or coloured ground on to which writing and attractive designs can be printed.

In its raw state the polystyrene is transparent. Something needs to be added to produce the white, opaque property.

Q4 What are the properties you would look for in a suitable additive to make a food package opaque? ◆

Paints and plastics, even if coloured by dyes, require a white background to reflect light. Look again at the refractive indexes shown in Table 4.2. Listed at the bottom are three substances we don't normally associate with food. Diamond is well known for its hardness and inertness, and its use as a gemstone. It is the high refractive index that gives a suitably cut diamond its sparkling quality, known as fire. Zirconia is often used in jewellery as a diamond substitute, but it also has limited use as a white pigment in paints and plastics. Rutile (titanium dioxide – TiO_2) is a cheap, non-toxic solid with a high refractive index of between 2.6 and 2.9. It is the commonest choice of white pigment for paints, plastics and ceramics.

 Look around your room. How many examples of paint and plastic with a white pigment base can you find? Don't forget to include coloured examples.

Almost everything that is coloured will contain a white pigment base.

Exploration 5.6 Making a mirror

10 MINUTES

Apparatus:

◆ sheet of clear plastic such as Perspex ◆ sheet of matte black paper

Take a sheet of Perspex and hold it up to a well lit wall. What do you see? Now place a sheet of matte black paper behind the plastic. What do you see now?

Against a bright background, and if it is not lit, the plastic should appear completely transparent. We see the transmitted light as it is brighter than the reflected light. On the other hand when no light is coming through the plastic it appears to behave like a mirror. It is the reflected light we notice. An interface between surfaces can transmit and reflect light.

In Section 4.6 'Why is milk white?' you saw that refraction occurred at the surfaces of the oil droplets in the milk, and that this could explain the white colour. It isn't just the refraction that produces high reflectivity, but also the reflection of light at the surfaces. At the boundary between two materials of different refractive index, a reflection occurs. Figure 5.6 shows an interface between two substances of different refractive index. If we define the intensity of light falling on the interface as I_0, the intensity reflected as I_r, and the intensity transmitted through the material as I_t. Then the fraction of light reflected is ρ (rho)

$$\rho = \frac{I_r}{I_0}$$

$$= \left(\frac{n_1 - n_2}{n_1 + n_2} \right)^2$$

(*Note:* Remember that n_1 is the refractive index of the first medium and n_2 is the refractive index for the medium that the light passes into.)

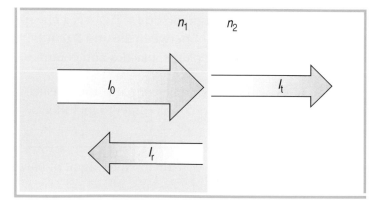

Figure 5.6 Reflection of light at an interface

And the fraction transmitted is τ (tau)

$$\tau = \frac{I_t}{I_0}$$
$$= 1 - \rho$$

(ρ is known as the reflection coefficient and τ is known as the absorption coefficient.)

Q5 What fractions of light are transmitted and reflected for a ray incident on a plane surface between (a) the water ($n = 1.33$) and oil ($n = 1.46$) in milk, (b) air ($n = 1.00$) and titanium dioxide ($n \approx 2.75$)?

Do you think this effect makes a significant contribution to the properties of milk and white plastic? ◆

In *The Invisible Man* by H. G. Wells (first published in 1897), two characters discuss the properties of glass.

'And here is another fact you will know to be true. If a sheet of glass is smashed Kemp, and beaten to a powder, it becomes much more visible while it is in air; it becomes at last an opaque white powder. This is because the powdering multiplies the surfaces of the glass at which refraction and reflection occur. But if the white powdered glass is put into water, it forthwith vanishes. The powdered glass and water have much the same refractive index; that is, the light undergoes very little refraction or reflection in passing from one to the other.

'Griffin makes a dramatic escape' (illustration by Louis Strimpl, 1912)

'You make the glass invisible by putting it into a liquid of nearly the same refractive index; a transparent thing becomes invisible if it is put in any medium of almost the same refractive index. And if you will consider only a second, you will see also that the powder of glass might be made to vanish in air, if its refractive index could be made the same as that of air; for then there would be no refraction or reflection as the light passed from glass to air.'

'Yes, yes,' said Kemp. 'But a man's not powdered glass!'

'No,' said Griffin. 'He's more transparent!'

(H. G. Wells, *The Invisible Man*)

20
MINUTES

Exploration 5.7   Making glass disappear

Apparatus:

◆ microscope slides   ◆ emery cloth   ◆ glass beaker

Give one microscope slide a ground glass appearance by rubbing for a few minutes with emery cloth.

Look through an empty beaker from the side with no writing, so that you see the reversed word PYREX on the far side.

What do you see when you hold (a) the ground glass slide in the middle of the beaker, (b) a plain slide in the middle of the beaker?

Now fill the beaker with water and place each slide in turn in the middle of the beaker as before.

Now what do you see through (a) the ground glass slide (b) the plain slide.

The results to the first part of the exploration should not be too surprising as the ground glass scatters light and makes it very hard or impossible to read anything through it. In the second part of the exploration the ground glass slide appears to let light through almost unchanged and you can read the word through it.

 Why does the ground glass now appear to not affect light?

> The refractive index of the water that surrounds the slide is very nearly the same as the glass of the slide, unlike the air from the first part. Light passes through this almost undeviated.

5.6 Toast: a burning issue

Most of us will have burnt toast, at least on one occasion. Some of us have managed it many times and have annoyed the others at home by setting off the smoke detector. This can take the enjoyment out of a quick snack.

In the infrared region of the electromagnetic spectrum bread has a reflection coefficient, ρ, of 0.95.

 What is the bread's absorption coefficient, τ, at these wavelengths?

> The absorption coefficient is $1 - \tau = 1 - 0.95 = 0.05$

At the start of toasting, a slice of white bread will absorb only 5% of the infrared radiation falling on it. So it heats up slowly. The radiation absorbed (which will also include some visible and UV wavelengths) causes a series of reactions in the surface of the bread. In these reactions the amine groups in protein chains combine with glucose molecules. We call this the Maillard reaction or glycation. The reaction products absorb light in the yellow to blue region of the spectrum, making the toast look brown. The increased absorption causes the toast to heat up more quickly and more glycation takes place. This, in turn, makes the toast more absorbent still, and it soon reaches a temperature where another reaction takes place. Now carbohydrate is oxidized to carbon. We recognize this because the toast turns black and is burnt.

By this point the values of the reflection coefficient and the absorption coefficient have swapped from their values for bread. The black toast absorbs 95% of the radiation falling on it and in a very short time it is oxidized all the way through.

If you have not yet smelled the burning, the flames that follow may catch your attention.

5.7 Food colouring and eye-catching containers

In the previous section you learnt that if we add substances to transparent materials it can give them an opaque appearance, which allows us to print bright coloured lettering and designs on to an otherwise featureless package.

What do we mean by colour? The majority of us grow up being able to see and distinguish all the colours of the rainbow. But the fact that we can distinguish these colours as separate shades is purely an effect of our perceptions. The only difference between these colours is the frequency of the electromagnetic radiation wave involved.

What do we mean when we say an object is black? At visible wavelengths coal appears black to us because it is absorbing electromagnetic energy at visible wavelengths. In fact, coal is also absorbing quite well at wavelengths from the ultraviolet, through the infrared and, to some extent, into the microwave region. But it may not absorb well at all wavelengths. We said that a coal fire is close to being a black body, but we need to qualify this. Look again at Figure 3.7 on page 43. The total range of wavelengths over which the black body would radiate is enormous. Even for the 700 K curve, the range over which significant energy is emitted is from the far infrared to the far ultraviolet. A black printing ink, on the other hand, may appear black to us because it absorbs light strongly in the visible region while in other regions of the spectrum it may be completely transparent.

Exploration 5.8 The jelly experiment

Apparatus:

- ◆ packet of red jelly cubes ◆ sharp knife ◆ green or blue LED and phototransistor
- ◆ circuit ◆ multimeter ◆ tile for cutting jelly

This exploration needs to be done in a darkened room. The voltage at the detector without a piece of jelly between the LED and the phototransistor is V_0 and with a piece of jelly is V_j. The aim here is to find the relationship between the voltage at the detector and the thickness of the jelly, x. Since both of these voltages depend on x we can show this by referring to them as V_{0x} and V_{jx}. V_{0x} will change as the LED and detector are moved further apart. (See Figure 5.7.)

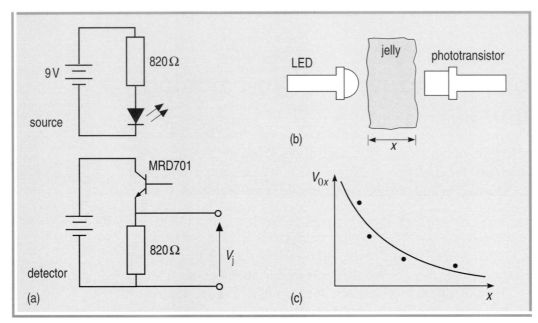

Figure 5.7 (a) Circuits for the jelly experiment, (b) LED and phototransistor arrangement, (c) rough shape of expected graph

Take readings for a range of thicknesses of jelly and plot $\dfrac{V_{jx}}{V_{0x}}$ against x.

For each reading of V_{jx}, have the LED and phototransistor just touching the jelly.

Draw a smooth curve as the line of best fit.

The curve that we would expect you to get from this experiment is shown in Figure 5.7(c). The voltage measured is an indication of the intensity of the light falling on the LED. A graph of intensity versus thickness of jelly will give the same shape of curve. This shape is frequently found in all science as it is a pattern that is widespread through the world around us. We call it an **exponential decay** curve and you will come across it again in the SLIPP units *Physics in Space* and *Physics Phones Home*.

Figure 5.8 shows the main feature of this curve. For the value y to drop to half its original value you move 20 units along the x-axis. Moving another 20 units along the x-axis produces a further halving of y, and so on. As a result the curve never quite reaches the x-axis. (*Note:* The scales shown in Figure 5.8 do not relate to your exploration.)

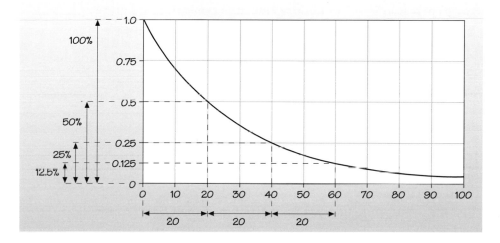

Figure 5.8
An exponential decay curve

The intensity of light that is transmitted through the jelly and produces the voltage V_{jx} is I_{tx}. The intensity of light received by the detector when touching the LED is I_0. The relationship between I_{tx} and I_0 is

$$\frac{I_{tx}}{I_0} = e^{-Ax} \tag{5.1}$$

(*Note:* You will not need to prove this relationship but you will need to be able to use it.)

Q6 A glass of diameter 8.0 cm is filled with a drink of absorption coefficient 1.25 m^{-1}. Light of intensity 0.50 W m^{-1} is falling on one side of the glass. What is the intensity of light emerging from the other side? ◆

A in Equation (5.1) is a constant and is known as the **absorption factor**. This is a property that varies between substances and depends on wavelength. For a coloured substance dissolved in another transparent material, such as a coloured dye dissolved in water, A also varies with the concentration. e is a constant number – to three decimal places it is 2.718.

e

The number e crops up in many of the patterns in nature, not just in exponential relationships. One set of logarithms is even based on e; these logarithms are called natural logarithms. If your calculator has an ln button it will also have an e^x function. To find e on your calculator find e^x for $x = 1$.

Remind yourself of the *law of conservation of energy*. What is happening to the energy of the light that is not transmitted through the jelly? If you place an absorbing object in strong light (such as sunlight), how might you demonstrate that the energy is conserved?

Light that is not transmitted by the jelly is absorbed and the energy that it carried is transferred to the chemical structure of the jelly, making its temperature increase by increasing the kinetic energy of its particles.

To demonstrate this you would need to choose a suitable object whose temperature you can measure and see if putting it in a strong light produces a temperature rise. If you wanted to show that this was due to visible frequencies you would need to filter out the infrared and ultraviolet from the incident light. You would also have to make sure the air temperature was constant.

Q7 (a) Given that $\ln\left(e^x\right) = x$ (rather like $\sin^{-1}(\sin\theta) = \theta$) rearrange

$$\frac{I_{tx}}{I_0} = e^{-Ax} \text{ to give } \ln\left(\frac{I_{tx}}{I_0}\right) = -Ax.$$

(b) A new jelly has an absorption factor of $2\ \text{m}^{-1}$ for infrared light. What thickness of jelly is needed over ice-cream to reduce the amount of infrared that it receives to 25% of the incident radiation? Would this be effective in stopping the ice-cream from melting? (*Hint:* You will need to use the equation that you derived in (a) to answer this part of the question.) ◆

Q8 Sir Archibald Wobble runs a very successful factory making jelly babies. But he is mean, and worries about the cost of food colours used in the manufacturing process. As an astute businessman, however, he recognizes that the public will not buy jelly babies unless they are brightly coloured. Outline a method for use on his production line to check that the amount of colour added is within his specified limits. ◆

We said that the absorption factor depends on wavelength, but why? To understand this we need to understand what is happening to molecules in a substance when electromagnetic energy is absorbed.

In the near infrared, visible and ultraviolet regions of the spectrum, the absorption of electromagnetic energy is due to changes in the way electrons are distributed within the atom or molecule, or, more accurately, changes in the **electronic states** of atoms and molecules. We say these are **electronic transitions**. One of the consequences of the development of **quantum mechanics** was the understanding that electrons in atoms and molecules are bound in **discrete energy levels** (Figure 5.9). The arrangement of all the electrons in the atom or molecule is its state. These states are altered when a photon is absorbed by the molecule, giving up its energy to that molecule.

When a photon of light energy is absorbed, the molecule in the lowest state (the **ground state**) jumps to higher **energy levels** (an **excited state**). But this can occur only if the photon energy is exactly equal to the energy gap between these states as shown in Figure 5.9.

$$E_2 - E_g = hf$$

or more generally

$$E_2 - E_1 = hf$$

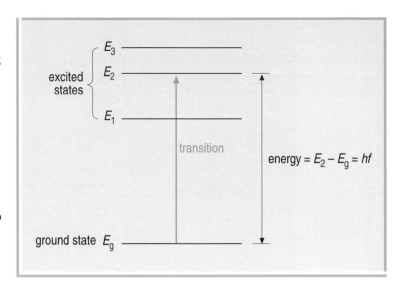

Figure 5.9
The energy levels of electrons and the absorption of a photon

The jump from one state to the other is called a **transition**.

The excited state is unstable, and after a short period of time the molecule can return to its ground state. To do this it must lose the extra energy it gained from the absorbed photon by emitting another, usually of the same energy (a process known as **emission**). However, some materials are able to absorb photons of invisible light and emit not just one but more than one photon. Although the total energy emitted is the same as that of the photon absorbed, each of the photons emitted are of lower energy. As they are of lower energy they are of lower frequency (or longer wavelength) and may be in the visible spectrum. This process is responsible for **fluorescence** and **phosphorescence**. In atoms this absorption process results in very sharp **absorption bands**, but in molecules the lines are much broader. There are two reasons for this. First, the energy levels are more complex, and several transitions may lie close to each other. Second, vibrations of the atoms making up the molecule couple with the electronic transitions to produce much more broad transitions. Figure 5.10 overleaf shows some electronic absorption spectra of typical molecules found in food. Chlorophyll is, of course, the substance we associate with green plants. Cyanocobalamin is vitamin B_{12}. The third example is a food colour, E155 (also known as brown HT).

Q9 What are the colours associated with the wavelengths of the absorption bands in these three compounds? What colours are transmitted by each of these compounds? ◆

Q10 We might use the food colouring E155 to colour icing sugar pink. What is happening to the colours of the incident white light, in terms of reflection and absorption, that results in the reflected light from the sugar appearing this colour? ◆

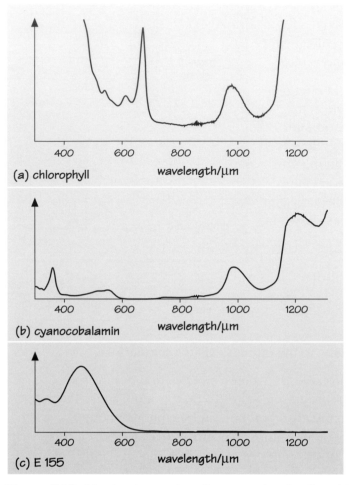

Figure 5.10 Electronic spectra of some molecules found in food: (a) chlorophyll, (b) cyanocobalamin (vitamin B_{12}), (c) E155

The printed colours on packets of food

Printing inks are generally carbon compounds designed by chemists to have very intense absorption bands in the visible part of the spectrum. Hence colour printing is a 'subtractive' process. In order to produce the effect of a given colour, all the other colours in the visible spectrum are subtracted from the light reflected from the package.

The package may be the titanium dioxide loaded polystyrene of a plastic carton, or may be white coated paper or cardboard. The white coating is produced by a layer of china clay or a white ink largely composed of titanium dioxide). White light falling on the package passes through the thin film of ink, is reflected from a white base material, and passes through the ink a second time. Light is absorbed at the wavelengths covered by the absorption bands of the ink, and the remaining wavelengths are little affected. For example, to produce red colour, all wavelengths shorter than about 580 nm must be absorbed.

How would you make a black box?

By mixing a number of dyes whose absorption bands cover the whole visible spectrum.

To produce packages that are 'whiter than white', fluorescent compounds are often added to the white pigment. Light absorbed in the blue and UV regions is re-emitted at longer, visible wavelengths giving a brighter appearance to whites and colours. Figure 5.11 shows the effects of mixing coloured pigments and the colour mixing for light that you should already be familiar with. Note the differences.

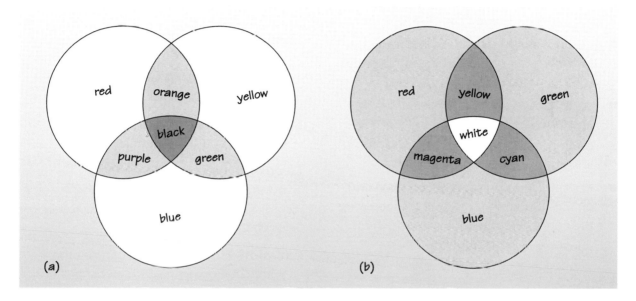

Figure 5.11 Colour mixing: (a) pigment, (b) light

Achievements

After working through this section you should be able to:

- interpret force versus extension graphs, identifying the limit of proportionality, elastic limit and yield point

- find the force or elastic constant, k, from a force versus extension graph

- interpret stress versus strain graphs, identifying the limit of proportionality, elastic limit and yield point

- find the Young modulus from a stress versus strain graph

- describe what is meant by the terms 'polymeric', 'crystalline' and 'amorphous' (or 'non-crystalline')

- correctly use the terms 'elastic', 'brittle' and 'ductile'

- describe surface colours in terms of absorbed and reflected light

- explain how photons are absorbed and emitted from atoms and molecules using the concept of energy levels and the equation $E_2 - E_1 = hf$.

Glossary

Absorption bands   Portions of the electromagnetic spectrum that are absorbed by a substance.

Absorption factor   The quantity relating the amount of electromagnetic energy absorbed to the amount incident.

Amorphous   A substance whose structure is not ordered. Also known as non-crystalline.

Brittle   A material that breaks before its elastic limit is reached.

Crystalline   A substance that is highly ordered at the atomic level, with regularly arranged atoms, molecules or ions.

Discrete energy levels   Separated energy levels. There can only be particular values.

Ductile   A material that breaks after passing its elastic limit, during plastic extension.

Elastic   An elastic material is one that will return to its original shape if it is deformed and then released.

Elastic constant   The slope of the initial straight portion of a force versus extension graph. Also known as force constant.

Elastic limit   On a force versus extension graph or a stress versus strain graph this is the point up to which the material is elastic and after which it is plastic.

Electronic states   The configuration of electrons in atoms or molecules.

Electronic transitions   Changes occurring in the electronic states of atoms or molecules when photons are absorbed or emitted.

Emission   The production of a photon when an atom or molecule changes state.

Energy level   The unique energy of a particle in a given state.

Excited state   A state of an atom or molecule above its ground state.

Exponential decay   A relationship between two variables where if one is constantly increased by a fixed *amount* the other will decrease by a fixed *proportion* each time.

Fluorescence   When an object exposed to light seems to glow with an extra bright colour, particularly in ultraviolet light, it is fluorescing. The ultraviolet light, which we cannot see, is absorbed and re-emitted at a wavelength that we can see.

Ground state   The lowest energy state of an atom or molecule.

Hooke's law   The deformation of a material will be proportional to the force applied as long as the deformation is small (the limit of proportionality is not exceeded).

Limit of proportionality   The limit of force or extension beyond which Hooke's law no longer applies; the end of the initial straight part of a force versus extension graph.

Organic polymer   A polymer made of organic molecules, i.e. molecules based on the carbon atom.

Phosphorescence   When an object glows (emits light) after a light source to which it has been exposed is withdrawn, it is displaying phosphorescence. The process is similar to fluorescence.

Plastic   This is the opposite to elastic. If a material is deformed and does not return to its original shape it is plastic.

Polymer   A substance made up of long chains of identical molecules, e.g. polythene (polyethylene), polyvinylchloride (PVC) and polystyrene.

Quantum mechanics   The theory of mechanics that describes the behaviour of photons of electromagnetic radiation as well as atomic and subatomic particles.

Strain   The ratio of the length of the deformation of a material under stress to its original length. (No unit.)

Stress   Unit: newton metre^{-2} (N m^{-2}) or pascal (Pa). The force per unit of cross-sectional area of a material.

Transition   Changes occurring in the states of atoms or molecules when photons are absorbed or emitted.

Young modulus   Unit: pascal (Pa) or newton metre^{-2} (N m^{-2}). A measure of the elasticity of a material. It is the ratio of tensile stress to strain evaluated within the linear part of the stress versus strain graph for a particular material. The higher the value of the Young modulus, the stiffer (more rigid) the material. (Also called tensile modulus and modulus of elasticity.)

Answers to Ready to Study test

R1

Work done = force × distance

$$= 20\,\text{N} \times 8\,\text{m}$$

$$= 160\,\text{J}$$

(*Note:* The mass plays no part in this calculation.)

R2

(a) Red, orange, yellow, green, blue, indigo and violet.

(b) (i) violet, (ii) red

(c)

$$c = f\lambda$$

$$f = \frac{c}{\lambda}$$

For violet light

$$f = \frac{3.0 \times 10^8 \,\text{ms}^{-1}}{4.0 \times 10^{-7}\,\text{m}}$$

$$= 7.5 \times 10^{14}\,\text{Hz}$$

For red light

$$f = \frac{3.0 \times 10^8 \, \text{ms}^{-1}}{7.0 \times 10^{-7} \, \text{m}}$$

$$= 4.3 \times 10^{14} \, \text{Hz (to two significant figures)}$$

R3

$$\text{Power} = \frac{\text{energy transferred}}{\text{time taken}}$$

energy transferred

$$= \text{power} \times \text{time taken}$$

$$= 1.5 \times 10^3 \, \text{W} \times 3 \, \text{min} \times 60 \, \text{s min}^{-1}$$

$$= 2.7 \times 10^5 \, \text{J}$$

R4

$F = ma$

Weight $= mg$

(a) Weight $= 1 \, \text{kg} \times 10 \, \text{m s}^{-2}$

$$= 10 \, \text{N}$$

(b) Weight $= 0.150 \, \text{kg} \times 10 \, \text{m s}^{-2}$

$$= 1.5 \, \text{N}$$

(c) Weight $= 1.3 \, \text{kg} \times 10 \, \text{m s}^{-2}$

$$= 13 \, \text{N}$$

R5

(a) Blue and green light mix to give cyan.

(b) Red, blue and green light mix to give white.

(c) Red and green light mix to give yellow.

To check, look very closely at your television screen, but make sure you are looking at pure colours.

R6

$E = hf$

$$= 6.6 \times 10^{-34} \, \text{J s} \times 6.0 \times 10^{-14} \, \text{Hz}$$

$$= 3.96 \times 10^{-47} \, \text{J}$$

$$= 4.0 \times 10^{-47} \, \text{J (to two significant figures)}$$

Answers to questions in the text

Q1

(a) (i) Energy transferred, E, in travelling to and from the supermarket is given by:

$$E = \text{power} \times \text{time taken}$$

$$= 50 \times 10^3 \, \text{W} \times 20 \, \text{min} \times 60 \, \text{s min}^{-1}$$

$$= 6.0 \times 10^7 \, \text{J (to two significant figures)}$$

(ii) For the soup, energy transferred, E_s, is given by:

$$E_s = 1.2 \times 10^3 \, \text{W} \times 3 \, \text{min} \times 60 \, \text{s min}^{-1}$$

$$= 2.2 \times 10^5 \, \text{J (to two significant figures)}$$

For the pizza, energy transferred, E_p, is given by:

$$E_p = 1.2 \times 10^3 \, \text{W} \times 5 \, \text{min} \times 60 \, \text{s min}^{-1}$$

$$= 3.6 \times 10^5 \, \text{J (to two significant figures)}$$

So the total energy transferred in cooking the food was $(2.2 + 3.6) \times 10^5 \, \text{J} = 5.8 \times 10^5 \, \text{J}$

The energy transferred in collecting the food is more than 100 times greater than the energy transferred in cooking it.

(b) The total energy available from the food was $524 \, \text{kJ} + 1000 \, \text{kJ} + 2000 \, \text{kJ} = 3.5 \times 10^6 \, \text{J}$

Q2

(a)

$$F = ke$$

so

$$k = \frac{F}{e}$$

$$= \frac{28\,\text{N}}{0.9 \times 10^{-3}\,\text{m}}$$

$$= 3 \times 10^4\,\text{Nm}^{-1} \text{ (to one significant figure)}$$

(b) The work done in stretching the wire to A is the area under the curve to this point. As it is a straight line

$$\text{energy stored in spring} = \frac{1}{2}Fe$$

$$= \frac{1}{2} \times 28\,\text{N} \times 0.9 \times 10^{-3}\,\text{m}$$

$$= 1 \times 10^{-2}\,\text{J}$$

$$\text{(to one significant figure)}$$

Q3

(a)

$$F = ke$$

so

$$k = \frac{F}{e}$$

$$= \frac{10\,\text{N}}{0.15 \times 10^{-3}\,\text{m}}$$

$$= 6.7 \times 10^4\,\text{Nm}^{-1}$$

$$\text{(to two significant figures)}$$

(b)

If we think of this wire as three wires identical to A joined end to end, then each one will extend by 0.15 m. So the total extension is $3 \times 0.15\,\text{mm} = 0.45\,\text{mm}$.

(c)

$$k = \frac{F}{e}$$

$$= \frac{10\,\text{N}}{4.5 \times 10^{-4}\,\text{m}}$$

$$= 2.2 \times 10^4\,\text{Nm}^{-1}$$

$$\text{(to two significant figures)}$$

(d) If we think of this wire as four wires identical to A with the force shared equally between them, we can consider just one of these to find e.

$$e = \frac{F}{k}$$

$$= \frac{10\,\text{N}}{4} \times \frac{1.0}{6.7 \times 10^4\,\text{Nm}^{-1}}$$

$$= 3.73 \times 10^{-5}\,\text{m}$$

$$= 3.7 \times 10^{-5}\,\text{m} \text{ (to two significant figures)}$$

(e) To find k we must consider the whole wire

$$k = \frac{F}{e}$$

$$= \frac{10\,\text{N}}{3.73 \times 10^{-5}\,\text{m}}$$

$$= 2.7 \times 10^5\,\text{Nm}^{-1} \text{ (to two significant figures)}$$

(f)

$$\text{Strain} = \frac{e}{L}$$

so

$$\text{strain of wire A} = \frac{0.15 \times 10^{-3}\,\text{m}}{1.0\,\text{m}}$$

$$= 1.5 \times 10^{-4}$$

strain of wire B $= \dfrac{0.45 \times 10^{-3}\,\text{m}}{3.0\,\text{m}}$

$= 1.5 \times 10^{-4}$

strain of wire C $= \dfrac{3.73 \times 10^{-5}\,\text{m}}{1.0\,\text{m}}$

$= 3.73 \times 10^{-5}$

(g)

$\text{Stress} = \dfrac{F}{A}$

so

stress for wire A $= \dfrac{10\,\text{N}}{0.50 \times 10^{-6}\,\text{m}^2}$

$= 2.0 \times 10^7\,\text{N}\,\text{m}^{-2}$

stress for wire B $= \dfrac{10\,\text{N}}{0.50 \times 10^{-6}\,\text{m}^2}$

$= 2.0 \times 10^7\,\text{N}\,\text{m}^{-2}$

stress for wire C $= \dfrac{10\,\text{N}}{2.0 \times 10^{-6}\,\text{m}^2}$

$= 5.0 \times 10^6\,\text{N}\,\text{m}^{-2}$

(h)

$E = \dfrac{\text{stress}}{\text{strain}}$

so

E for wire A $= \dfrac{2.0 \times 10^7\,\text{N}\,\text{m}^{-2}}{1.5 \times 10^{-4}}$

$= 1.3 \times 10^{11}\,\text{N}\,\text{m}^{-2}$

E for wire B $= \dfrac{2.0 \times 10^7\,\text{N}\,\text{m}^{-2}}{1.5 \times 10^{-4}}$

$= 1.3 \times 10^{11}\,\text{N}\,\text{m}^{-2}$

E for wire C $= \dfrac{5.0 \times 10^6\,\text{N}\,\text{m}^{-2}}{3.73 \times 10^{-5}}$

$= 1.3 \times 10^{11}\,\text{N}\,\text{m}^{-2}$

Therefore the Young modulus is a property of the metal and not of the particular arrangement.

Q4

The additive would need to block the transmission of light, and it should not be toxic or adversely alter the properties of the container it colours.

Q5

$\rho = \dfrac{I_r}{I_0}$

$= \left(\dfrac{n_1 - n_2}{n_1 + n_2} \right)^2$

(a) Between water and oil:

fraction of light reflected is

$\rho = \left(\dfrac{1.33 - 1.46}{1.33 + 1.46} \right)^2$

$= (-0.04659)^2$

$= 0.00217$

$= 2.17 \times 10^{-3}$ or 0.217%

(to three significant figures)

fraction of light transmitted is

$\tau = 1 - \rho$

$= 0.99783$

$= 0.998$ or 99.8%

(to three significant figures)

(b) Between air and titanium dioxide:

fraction of light reflected is

$$\rho = \left(\frac{1.00 - 2.75}{1.00 + 2.75}\right)^2$$

$$= 0.218 \text{ or } 21.8\%$$

fraction of light transmitted is

$$\tau = 1 - \rho$$

$$= 0.782 \text{ or } 78.2\%$$

(to three significant figures)

From the values calculated this effect would be insignificant for milk – it is refraction rather than reflection that is responsible for its optical qualities. For the air and titanium dioxide interface, reflection is an important effect.

Q6

$$\frac{I_{tx}}{I_0} = e^{-Ax}$$

so

$$I_{tx} = I_0 e^{-Ax}$$

$$= 0.50 \text{ W m}^{-1} \times e^{\left(-1.25\text{m}^{-1} \times 8.0 \times 10^{-2}\text{ m}\right)}$$

$$= 0.45 \text{ W m}^{-1}$$

Q7

(a)

$$\frac{I_{tx}}{I_0} = e^{-Ax}$$

$$\ln\left(\frac{I_{tx}}{I_0}\right) = \ln\left(e^{-Ax}\right)$$

but since

$$\ln\left(e^{-Ax}\right) = -Ax$$

then

$$\ln\left(\frac{I_{tx}}{I_0}\right) = -Ax$$

(b) For jelly of thickness x,

$$x = -\frac{\ln\left(I_{tx}/I_0\right)}{A}$$

$$= -\frac{\ln\left(25/100\right)}{2\text{m}^{-1}}$$

$$= \frac{1.386}{2\text{m}^{-1}}$$

$$= 0.693\text{m}$$

$$\approx 50\text{cm}$$

This would definitely reduce the heating of the ice-cream directly from the infrared. This energy would be absorbed by the jelly instead. The temperature of the jelly would rise and energy would be conducted and radiated from the jelly to its surroundings. As the ice-cream forms only part of the jelly's surroundings it would be heated less than had the jelly not been there.

If this is how a manufacturer intends to use jelly we would recommend that they find one with a much higher absorption coefficient – having to eat through a 50 cm thick jelly before getting to the ice-cream would defeat most people!

Q8

First, samples of jelly should be made using different concentrations of the colour. Then slices of identical size should be cut and measured in apparatus like that used in Exploration 5.8. A calibration chart of potential difference against concentration can then be plotted. Now, samples of jelly babies can be tested by slicing them to the same size as the original samples and measuring their potential differences in the apparatus. The potential differences can then be found on the chart and the unknown concentrations read off. If the concentrations are within Sir Archibald's specified limits then all is well.

Q9

For chlorophyll, the highest energy bands are in the blue and ultraviolet. Lower down the bands are in the red and infrared. Therefore, only green and yellow light is transmitted. Cyanocobalamin appears weakly red as it absorbs mainly in the blue to green region of the spectrum. E155 absorbs mostly at the blue end, so it appears red.

Q10

Most of the incident light is reflected by the sugar. Some is absorbed by the food colour coating the particles, and so slightly more red light is reflected than the other colours.

Cooking involves biological materials undergoing a sequence of chemical reactions. As you may know from experiments in chemistry, most reactions take place more quickly at high temperature.

In cooking, the chemical changes are often complicated and sometimes require the temperature to be reasonably uniform throughout. When roasting meat, for example, the meat has to be kept at a steady temperature for perhaps 2 hours, enabling quite slow chemical changes to occur throughout. If the oven is too hot and the time too short, the same energy may be supplied, but the meat could be overcooked on the outside and undercooked inside. The situation is similar when baking cakes. The cake may appear cooked on the outside but still be 'sad' in the centre. And when grilling chops, the outside appears to be done after only about a minute, but in fact the chops will require about 10 minutes to cook through, by which time the outer surfaces may be looking dry and at risk of burning.

In this section, we look at the control of the cooking process, particularly temperature and timing.

READY TO STUDY TEST

Before you begin this section you should be able to:

■ describe latent heat and use it to explain why temperature does not change as a substance is changing state

■ give details of the two types of charged particles in atoms

■ measure potential difference and current in a circuit and find the resistance

■ give the link between the temperature of a substance and the average kinetic energy of its particles

■ describe solids, liquids and gases in terms of their particles.

QUESTIONS

R1 Why doesn't the temperature of pure boiling water rise above 100°C and what do we call the energy needed to make water vaporize at 100°C?

R2 (a) What is the name of the negatively charged particle in an atom? (b) What are the names of the other particles? (c) What can you say about their charges?

R3 Name the instruments that are used to measure current and potential difference. Draw a circuit to show how these are used. What can you say about the resistances of these instruments?

R4 Describe how you would use these devices to find the resistance of a piece of resistance wire.

IN CONTROL

6.1 The need for control

Many cooking processes rely on boiling, which is a very dependable temperature control. Pure water boils at 100°C. Water containing salt or other materials dissolved from the food will boil at a slightly higher temperature, but no matter how high you turn up the control on the hob, the temperature of the boiling water will not change. The rate of evaporation will change. Hence rapid boiling will increase the rate of use of energy but will not significantly increase the rate of cooking. There is one way to speed up this method of cooking – use a pressure cooker as described in Section 3.2.

The temperature of an oven can be pre-set to one of a whole range of values. This relies on a thermostat to limit the rate of supply of energy when the selected temperature has been reached.

Consequently, it is usually safe to leave items roasting, baking or stewing in an oven, or boiling on a stove, for a certain length of time, knowing that they will not burn.

The same cannot be said for shallow frying or grilling, which need constant attention, to ensure that things are not overcooked and possibly burned. Deep frying is reasonably stable as the cooking process tends to control the temperature. For example, when cooking chips, the structure of potatoes is broken down and releases water. The evaporation of this water constantly takes energy from the cooking oil, and this keeps the temperature well below the boiling point of oil. (This does not, of course, mean that it is safe to leave chip pans unattended – if oil does escape from the pan, because of vigorous boiling of the water from the potatoes, it will probably catch fire, with disastrous consequences.)

Items left in an oven or on a stove could be cooked too long. There is usually an ideal time although it is not particularly critical. Few of us have the confidence to leave items cooking for a pre-set time without some intermediate inspection. We look at the roast meat and turn it over, give the casserole a stir, stick a skewer in the sponge cake or a fork in the potatoes.

Yet industrial cooking *has* to be done this way. For example, large bakeries produce bread, cakes and biscuits, using ovens without doors. They have long chain conveyors carrying the food at a slow speed through the oven. So it goes in uncooked at one end, and comes out cooked at the other. The length of the oven is constant, perhaps about 10 metres, so the speed of the conveyor then determines the time that the food is in the oven. No opportunity for immediate inspection here! The local corner shop bakers will not have a conveyor system, but their ovens are larger than in a domestic kitchen. Regular practice enables them to know the exact time to leave items cooking, and intermediate inspection is unlikely, but with many items to bake during the same night it is likely that they will have timers on their ovens.

With your home cooking, no matter how good your intentions, there is a possibility of being distracted, by a friend visiting, a good TV programme or the telephone ringing. This may cause the carrots to boil dry or the cakes to burn.

Many energy sources can be used for cooking. The earliest would have been a simple wood fire, while these days most of us obtain the energy for cooking from the mains supply of electricity or gas. There are, of course, other options: many Africans use dung and some people like to use solid fuel or oil in cooking ranges such as Agas and Rayburns.

Some of us think that efficient use of energy should come into our cooking plans to keep down the cost and to avoid waste of natural resources. So this section will be about measuring and controlling temperature, measuring time, and measuring energy consumption.

BOTULISM

Many micro organisms are present in the food we eat. Some only cause food to putrefy, and are readily dealt with by heat treatment or cooling. Others can cause food poisoning. *Clostridium botulinum* is one such organism. (A related organism *Clostridium tetani* is responsible for tetanus or 'lock-jaw'.) *Clostridium botulinum* occurs naturally in the intestines of herbivores and enters our food chain on the meat products from these animals. When allowed to grow in food the bacteria produce the most potent poison known, and it is this rather than the ingestion of the bacteria themselves that causes the disease. The symptoms of botulism develop between 2 and 36 hours after the food is eaten, and include gastrointestinal pain, headache, photophobia and double vision, weakness, constipation, respiratory difficulty and, in some cases, death from respiratory failure. Fortunately the disease is not common, affecting about 20 people per year in the USA, for example (about half of these cases

would be fatal). *C. botulinum* is difficult to irradicate from food. This is because of its ability to produce spores, a dormant form of the organism. Whereas the vegetative form of the bacteria is relatively easily killed by heat treatment (5 to 10 minutes at 70°C), the spores require much higher temperatures and/or longer times. This is important in a food process such as canning where the cans are heat treated after filling and sealing to reduce the bacterial numbers. *Clostridium botulinum* spores require 5 hours at 100°C to reduce their numbers to safe levels but only 4 minutes at 120°C. In order to check that the process is working correctly, sample cans are taken from the production line and the numbers of bacteria present are measured. Typically the organism measured is not *Clostridium botulinum* itself but a more resistant organism such as *Bacillus stearothermophilus*, which would require three times the length of sterilization needed to kill *Clostridium botulinum*. This allows an adequate safety margin.

6.2 Heating using electricity

For most of us electricity is one of the most familiar energy sources for cooking so we are now going to look at it more closely.

What we normally call electric current along wires is actually a movement of charged particles or, more precisely, a flow of electrons. If the terminals of a battery are connected by metal wires, an electric current flows: negatively charged electrons flow through the wires from the negative terminal to the positive terminal. Electrons flow to the positive terminal because their electrical energy is lower at that terminal. This is analogous to saying that an object will fall to the Earth when released, because this reduces the gravitational potential energy of the object.

The change in electrical energy when a charge moves from one position to another is determined by a quantity called the potential difference (also known as the voltage) between those two positions. The potential difference, V, is defined as the electrical energy difference per unit positive charge:

$$\text{potential difference} = \frac{\text{electrical energy difference}}{\text{charge}}$$

or, in symbols,

$$V = \frac{\Delta E_{el}}{q} \qquad\qquad (6.1)$$

The common unit of potential difference is the volt (denoted by the letter V), which is defined so that the potential difference between two places is exactly one volt if the transfer of one coulomb of positive charge between the two places requires an energy transfer of one joule. Or as an equation

1 volt = 1 joule per coulomb

$1\ \text{V} = 1\ \text{J C}^{-1}$

Why positive charge? When theories for electricity were first being formulated, Benjamin Franklin proposed that the electrical *fluid* flowed from the positive to the negative terminals of a supply. We continue to use this model and call it **conventional current**. Don't forget, though, that current is really moving negative electrons.

Equation (6.1) can be rearranged to get an expression for the amount of electrical energy transferred by a positive charge q moving through a potential difference V:

$\Delta E_{el} = qV$

Q1 When you start a car to go to the supermarket suppose that 250 coulombs of charge are transferred from the negative terminal of a 12-volt car battery via the starter motor to the positive terminal. What is the decrease in electrical energy of the electrons involved? ◆

This amount of electrical energy is transferred into the kinetic energy of the starter motor and engine, and into internal energy.

When you think about the operation of an electrical device, you probably don't consider how many electrons or how much charge flows through it. You are far more likely to consider the *rate* at which charge flows through it – in other words the electric current. Formally, the electric current in a circuit is defined as the amount of charge passing a given point per unit time. If a charge q flows past a particular point at a constant rate in time t, the current (normally denoted by I) is given by the equation

$$I = \frac{q}{t}$$

The SI unit of current is therefore one of $\dfrac{\text{charge}}{\text{time}}$, i.e. $C\ s^{-1}$. This unit is given the name ampere (often shortened to amp), and is denoted by the letter A:

$$1\ A = 1\ C\ s^{-1}$$

The electricity companies supply homes with the energy to move the charge (electrons) already in the conductors: all that consumers have to do is plug their gadgets into the mains supply and the moving charge makes energy available in that appliance. The potential difference of a consumer's mains supply is always the same, but different devices require charge to be delivered at different rates in order to operate them. The rate at which one form of energy can be transferred into another is given the name power. Provided the energy is being transferred at a constant rate,

$$\text{power} = \frac{\text{amount of energy transferred}}{\text{time taken for the transfer}}$$

Although we most often think of power in connection with electrical energy and the **power rating** of various electrical appliances, the above equation is quite general and can be used in any situation in which energy is transferred or transformed at a constant rate.

The SI unit of power is therefore one of $\dfrac{\text{energy}}{\text{time}}$, i.e. $J\ s^{-1}$. This unit is given the name watt, and is denoted by the letter W.

Q2 You have probably been asked to look at the power ratings marked on the electrical equipment in your home many times before. If so, place the following listed electrical items of equipment in order of increasing power rating (you will have to do some research if you haven't done this before): microwave, kettle, toaster, domestic light bulb. ◆

When you are using these pieces of household equipment, you should bear in mind that they are really just devices to transfer the energy of the charges flowing into them into forms of energy that can be used to do various jobs.

When a potential difference V is maintained across a conductor, a current I flows from one end to the other. The **resistance** of the conductor, R, is defined by

$$R = \frac{V}{I}$$

For metal wires, R is constant over a wide range of currents, and the above equation is usually called **Ohm's law**. This is not strictly true, however, Ohm actually wrote that:

> the current flowing in a conductor is directly proportional to the potential difference across it, as long as there is no change in its physical conditions $I \propto V$.

If R is constant, the current that flows through a conductor will be directly proportional to the potential difference (see Figure 6.1).

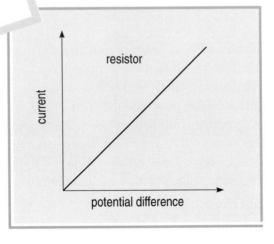

Figure 6.1 Graph of current versus potential difference for a resistance

The unit of resistance is the ohm (symbol Ω).

1 ohm = 1 volt ampere^{-1}

$1\ \Omega = 1\ \text{V A}^{-1}$

Ohm's law is not a fundamental law of physics to be regarded in the same way as, for example, Newton's second law. It is merely a useful relationship that is obeyed by most metals in normal circumstances and at constant temperature. It is not obeyed by all materials nor by all components in electrical circuits. $R = \dfrac{V}{I}$, however, can always be used.

6.3 Power revisited

We said earlier that in an electrical circuit negatively charged electrons flow through the wires from the negative terminal to the positive terminal. We believe that the electrons flow to the positive terminal because their electrical energy is lower at that terminal. So the electrons lose energy as they travel through the wire. But, of course, 'lost' energy does not just disappear. That would go against the principle of conservation of energy. Instead, it is transferred to the surrounding particles. The electrons are accelerated, gaining kinetic energy; this energy is subsequently lost through interactions with atoms in the metal, causing the atoms to vibrate more. The rate of loss of energy is easily found. If a charge Δq flows through a wire across which there is an applied potential difference V, then there is a loss of energy given by $\Delta q \times V$.

If Δq is measured in coulombs and V in volts, then to satisfy the above equation the units of energy must be in joules.

Now

$$\text{power} = \frac{\text{amount of energy transferred}}{\text{time taken for the transfer}}$$

$$= \frac{\Delta q V}{\Delta t}$$

But the rate of transfer of charge, $\dfrac{\Delta q}{\Delta t}$, is simply the average current, with 1 amp equal to 1 coulomb per second. So, in electrical circuits

$$\text{power}, P = IV$$

If I is measured in amps and V in volts, then the power will be in watts.

Q3 (a) A current I is flowing through a resistance R. Using the above equation for power and Ohm's law, find a way of expressing the equation for the power in terms of I and R.

(b) Use the first of these expressions to find the power dissipated when a current of 4 A flows through a resistance of 60 Ω. ◆

The electricity companies charge domestic customers for the amount of electrical energy they use. This is just the product of the power and the time. They do not use joules, but instead their bills are written in terms of kilowatt hours (kWh):

$$1 \text{ kW h} = 1 \text{ kilowatt} \times 1 \text{ hour}$$
$$= (1 \times 10^3 \text{ watts}) \times (3600 \text{ seconds})$$
$$= 3.6 \times 10^6 \text{ J or } 3.6 \text{ MJ}$$

Q4 A light bulb is rated at 60 W, an electric iron at 750 W and an oven at 2.0 kW. How many joules of electrical energy are converted when each of these devices is left on for an hour? ◆

If you have an electric cooker at home, or an electricity supply point next to a gas cooker that would allow you the option to change to electric cooking, it is most likely that the cable for this supply is separate from all the other supplies in the house, and uses thicker wire. Inspection of the circuit breaker or fuse box will quite likely reveal that the cooker has a 40 amp protection, but for the ring-main that runs all the other items in the house it is only 30 amp. An electric cooker demands a considerable current and the running cost appears as a substantial proportion of your electricity bill.

The following exploration could be done in most homes, school kitchens or possibly a lab.

 Exploration 6.1   Comparing the power of electric kettles and microwave ovens

Apparatus:

- ◆ electric kettle ◆ microwave oven ◆ measuring jug or measuring cylinder
- ◆ water ◆ microwaveable bowl (capacity at least 1 litre) ◆ stopwatch or clock with second hand ◆ thermometer (not essential)

The power rating of both the kettle and the microwave oven should be written somewhere on the appliances. Find this information and make a note of it. Measure half a litre of water from the cold tap into an empty kettle and into a microwaveable bowl. If you have a thermometer, measure the temperature of this water. Switch the kettle on and measure the time until the water boils. Switch the microwave on full and measure the time until the water boils. Estimate the increase in internal energy of the water using the equation

energy input = temperature rise× mass of water × specific heat capacity of water

The initial temperature of the water should be estimated as 12°C if you haven't measured it; 0.5 litre of water has a mass of 0.5 kg; the specific heat capacity of water is $4200 \, \mathrm{J \, kg^{-1} \, K^{-1}}$. Estimate the power input to the water for both the kettle and the microwave oven, using their electrical power ratings. Now estimate the efficiency of each of the appliances using the equation

$$\text{efficiency} = \frac{\text{useful power output}}{\text{power input}}$$

Compare the results for the two appliances. Discuss where energy is lost from the appliances.

The electrical power ratings on most appliances are approximate figures only. How might you modify this experiment to determine the actual electrical power consumed?

An electric cooker may be rated at 8 kW, which includes the oven, four rings and a grill. The current has to be available for all of them to be switched on at the same time. It would not be popular to have to turn off the grill in order to put on the oven, although in some cookers this is necessary.

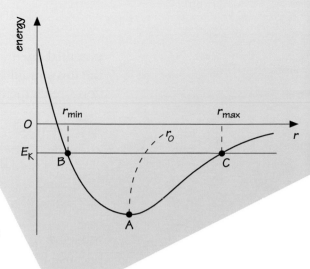

Figure 6.2
An energy well for a molecule

When we look at how we are charged for the supply of electrical energy, we see that the joule turns out to be a very small unit, which is why the kilowatt hour is much more useful for billing.

At the time of writing, the price for the supply of electrical energy is about 7p per kWh.

Gas supply is measured by the cubic metre (although the meter is likely to measure in cubic feet); if we then multiply the volume of gas used by the energy obtained by burning unit volume (usually called the **calorific value**, with units of $MJ\ m^{-3}$) the energy supply can be quoted in kW h.

At the time of writing, the price for gas supply is about 1.5p per kW h.

Q5 (a) On a gas bill, the calorific value was stated as $40\ MJ\ m^{-3}$ and the volume of gas supplied was $156\ m^3$, find the energy supplied in kW h. (b) If the standing charge was £9.50 and the cost of the gas was 1.5p per kW h, what was the total bill? ◆

6.4 The expanding cooking pot

As the temperature of a body rises, the kinetic energy of the atoms or molecules also rises – they vibrate faster and in general their amplitude of vibration will increase. An atom or molecule in a solid will have both kinetic energy (due to its motion) and potential energy (due to the forces acting on it from other atoms and molecules).

To help gain a clearer picture of what is happening, consider the atoms in a solid. Although the atoms have their own positions they are also moving. They vibrate around these positions with a kinetic energy that increases with temperature. The separation between the nuclei of these atoms is constantly changing about a mean distance. As the nuclei become close they repel each other and as they move further apart this force changes to attraction. These forces are due to the charges in the atoms.

Figure 6.2 illustrates this by showing the potential energy of a pair of atoms over a range of separations. Imagine you are holding an eraser and are pulling and pushing it so that its length changes. With no forced applied, the eraser will have a natural length r_0 on Figure 6.2. If you try to squash it you have to apply a force, and in squashing it you have stored potential energy in its structure. The greater the deformation, the greater the force required and the greater the energy stored. In the same way, if you stretch the eraser you store potential energy in its structure.

 What value of potential energy could we define as zero?

We could define the minimum energy as zero or, as in the molecular bond, we could choose another value. Here we could choose the energy stored just as the eraser snaps when fully stretched.

In Figure 6.2 you can see that the curve is not symmetrical. This is because it is harder to get molecules very close than it is to pull them apart. The zero energy level is chosen to be the potential energy of their bond when they are infinitely spaced. This shape of potential energy curve is often referred to as a **potential well**.

If you were able to ignore the third law of thermodynamics and cool the substance to absolute zero, the separation between the two atoms would be that at which the potential energy was at a minimum, shown as A on Figure 6.2. As the temperature is increased the kinetic energy with which the atoms vibrate also increases.

To help us now it is useful to think of a mass oscillating up and down on the end of a spring. At both the top and the bottom of its motion there is a moment when its speed and therefore kinetic energy is zero. At these points its potential energy is a maximum. The sum of the potential energy of the mass and its kinetic energy is constant but the amount of each of these is constantly changing. So at temperatures above absolute zero the gap between the two atoms is constantly changing. The maximum and minimum values of this separation are given from this graph by looking at the values for when all the energy in the bond is potential energy. This is shown in Figure 6.2 by the line BC, which corresponds to the maximum kinetic energy E_K of the atoms at a particular temperature.

All of this kinetic energy is stored as potential energy at two values of r given as r_{min} and r_{max}.

 The mid-point between r_{min} and r_{max}, r_0, is not the same as the separation at absolute zero. What does this mean?

This actually gives us an explanation of expansion. As the temperature increases so does the average separation between particles, which leads to an expansion of the material. This is due to the asymmetry of the curve.

The fractional increase in length is proportional to the increase in temperature. Typically, for a solid the increase is about one part in 100 000 for each degree rise in temperature. But this is by no means a constant for all materials; different materials have different rates of expansion, and you may well be familiar with ways in which this can be exploited. For example, if the lid of a jar is particularly tight it sometimes helps to put the jar under the hot tap – the hot water makes the metal lid expand more than the glass jar.

Some types of thermometer, and many thermostats, make use of the differences in **expansion coefficients** between the components of a **bimetallic strip**. This is discussed in the Section 6.5. Table 6.1 shows the expansion coefficients of various materials.

Table 6.1 Expansion coefficients of various materials at 20°C

Material	Expansion coefficient/10^{-6} K^{-1}
Aluminium	23.1
Copper	16.5
Pure iron	11.8
Cast iron	11.9
Stainless steel	9.5–11.1
Pyrex glass	2.8

(Source: *Tables of Physical and Chemical Constants*, 14th edn, 1973, p. 52)

 Can you think of a reason why stainless steel has a range of values for its expansion coefficient?

Stainless steel is an alloy containing iron, chromium, nickel and carbon. The particular proportions of these will determine the properties of the alloy.

6.5 Thermometers and thermostats

In an earlier section we discussed the meaning of temperature and temperature scales. Temperature can be measured with a thermometer, of course, but there are many kinds. You will almost certainly be familiar with the common mercury in glass thermometer. You do occasionally see these on old style ovens, but it is usually more convenient to have a solid thermometer.

A common type of thermometer makes use of the fact that different metals expand by different amounts when they are heated. Two similar sized strips of different metals are bonded together to make what is known as a bimetallic strip. When a straight bimetallic strip is heated, the metal that expands more will become longer than the other, and the only way for the metals to remain fixed together while this happens is if they form a curve with the more expansive metal on the outside.

If the bimetallic strip is formed in a coil shape, as the temperature changes the coil opens or closes. A pointer attached to the coil indicates the temperature (see Figure 6.3).

Such a thermometer is suitable for ovens and freezers (e.g. fixed in the door); it is inexpensive but not very accurate.

Figure 6.3
Using a bimetallic strip as a simple thermometer

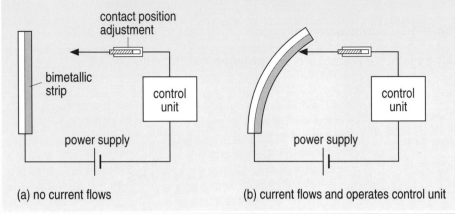

Figure 6.4 Using a bimetallic strip as a thermostat

Q6 As the temperature increases the pointer should move to the right. If copper and iron are used in the bimetallic spiral explain whether the copper should be on the inside or outside. ◆

The same effect can be used to make a simple temperature-dependent switch (a thermostat) as shown in Figure 6.4. At room temperature this bimetallic strip is straight, as its temperature rises it forms a curve

A bimetallic strip is also used to control the 'pop-up' mechanism of a toaster (see Figure 6.5).

The bread is placed in the toaster and the lever depressed to lower it between the main elements. This lever also depresses a metal catch, which closes the switch, and latches behind a swinging plate. Power through the main elements toasts the bread, and through the second element heats the bimetallic strip. As the strip heats it bends and causes the swinging plate to pivot about P. A point is reached when the swinging plate no longer prevents the metal catch moving up. The main spring pulls the catch plate upwards, opening the switch, and popping the toast out of the slot. The degree of toasting is controlled by adjusting the pre-load to the bimetallic strip.

Another type of thermometer in common use relies on the fact that electrical resistance changes with temperature. Increasing the temperature of metals increases their resistance, that is, conduction becomes more difficult. You should recall from the earlier section on conduction that metals are particularly good thermal and electrical

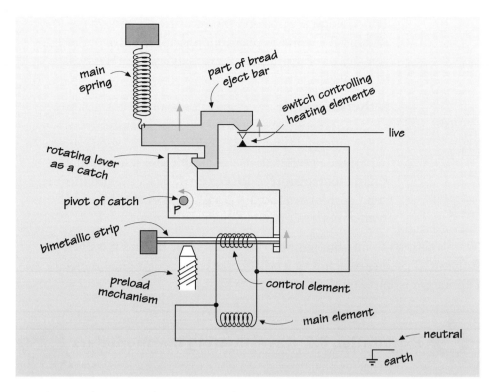

Figure 6.5
The pop-up mechanism of toaster

conductors because electrons are free to move around inside a metal. When the temperature of the metal increases, it becomes more difficult for the electrons to move between the atoms of the metal, because the atoms are vibrating more energetically.

A useful analogy here is trying to run along a corridor containing a number of people. If they stand still, it is relatively easy to pass between them. If they move about it is much more difficult.

The resistance to current in a metal is due to a vast array of irregular movements, so it seems unlikely that the change of resistance with temperature will be uniform; in fact, for platinum, copper and some other metals it actually is quite uniform, which is very good fortune! Figure 6.6 shows a graph of resistance versus temperature for copper.

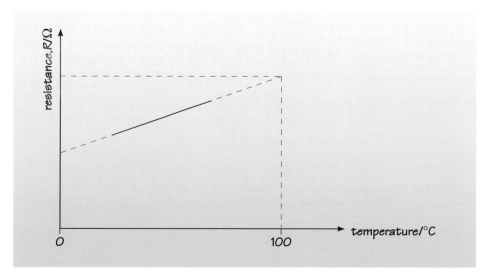

Figure 6.6
Graph showing how resistance changes with temperature for copper

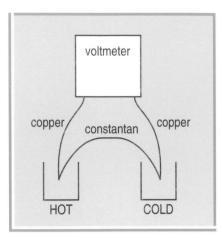

Figure 6.7
Thermocouple

For cooking purposes, a thermometer based on the above techniques with the platinum resistor in an oven and the remainder of the apparatus well away from the heat, would work well.

A **thermocouple** offers another option for providing an electrical response to changes in temperature. Two different metals are connected in a circuit (see Figure 6.7). When the two junctions are at different temperatures a small **electromotive force (emf)** is set up and this tries to send current around the circuit. The emf can be measured with a modern digital voltmeter.

The variation of emf with temperature is not uniform and it is even difficult to predict which way it will act for a particular pair of metals. So calibration is important.

Exploration 6.2   Investigating thermometers

30 MINUTES

With your group construct a chart or a computer database that gives a summary of the various kinds of thermometer. Don't limit yourself to the information that we have provided but look elsewhere to find out more about each one.

You will need to decide on the categories of information that you are going to include. Here are some suggestions: the particular thermal property that the thermometer uses, e.g. electrical resistance; the range of temperatures that it covers; whether the scale is linear or if there is another relationship; accuracy; the size of the thermometer. You should be able to add some more.

Exploration 6.3   Calibrating a thermocouple

40 MINUTES

Apparatus:

◆ thermocouple ◆ sand bath ◆ thermometer reading to about 300°C ◆ ice/water bath ◆ voltmeter ◆ Bunsen burner

Wrap one of the thermocouple junctions around the bulb of the thermometer and put it in the sand bath; put the other in the ice/water bath. Connect the ends to the voltmeter.

Heat the sand bath, slowing down as you near the limit of the thermometer. Stop heating and allow it to cool. As it cools take readings of the temperature and the voltmeter readings.

Plot a graph of voltmeter reading against temperature.

How do we use our thermometer to control the temperature of the gas or electric oven? Clearly we could stand and watch the temperature indicated by our thermometer (be it mechanical or electrical) with the electric power switched on or the gas lit, and when it reached the required temperature we could turn off the source of heat. We would then observe the temperature falling as the oven lost energy to its surroundings. When the temperature fell too low we could then turn the source of heat back on. This would be extremely tedious. What is more, if we had other things to do around the kitchen, like preparing other parts of the meal, feeding the cat and watching television, our attention might stray and the oven either overheat or cool down too much.

It would be better if we could ask a friend to do it for us. Or better still, a slave, who wouldn't disappear when the task got too boring! But they too might be distracted. We would prefer our slave always to attend to the task in hand and cost nothing to run. These requirements are fitted perfectly by the thermostat, a special case of a device called an **automaton**.

CYBERNETICS AND AUTOMATION

'Automatic' has become one of those words we frequently misuse. Nowadays we tend to think of it in the context of machinery, particularly those machines that carry out a sequence of operations without our intervention.

But its true origin lies in the development of the science of cybernetics (from the Greek *kybernetes* meaning a governor or steersman). This was developed in the late 1940s by the American mathematician Norbert Weiner from work carried out in the Second World War on mechanisms to control the direction of large guns. The automatic systems developed for this purpose form the basis of modern control circuits such as thermostats. The systems have some means of measuring temperature (the controlled variable), which is then used to create an analogue signal, e.g. a potential difference or, in the case of a mechanical thermostat, position. The size of this analogue signal depends on the size of the temperature and is then compared with a value representing the required temperature (command variable) by a controller. The output of the controller is an error signal, which adjusts the heating control – either up if the measured temperature is too low or down if too high. This loop of control is a feedback loop.

In cybernetics, an automaton is a machine (electrical, mechanical or biological) that uses information about its output to adjust its input to a desired value. An automatic washing machine uses feedback to regulate temperature, but all the controls for its cycle of wash and rinse are sequential and should not strictly be called automatic.

If you observe an electric cooker ring as it warms up, set at about three-quarters of its maximum setting, you will notice that as the element reaches the point of glowing, a click will be heard, and the glow will fade. After a few seconds another click will be heard and the element will begin to glow again. This process will repeat in order to maintain the temperature.

A typical mechanical controller will usually consist of a bimetallic element to sense the temperature. Its position corresponds to the actual temperature. As the temperature rises the strip will move to some position where it will activate a mechanism to reduce the energy input. As the temperature cools again the bimetallic strip moves back, and the heat input increases again. In a typical electric cooker the bimetallic strip opens a switch, cutting off power to the heating element. In a gas cooker a valve will be closed, reducing the gas flow. In each case a mechanical adjustment can be made so that the bimetallic strip cuts off the heat at the desired temperature. In more modern electronic systems the temperature analogue is a potential difference that is compared with another potential difference derived from the control knob. The output of this **comparator** is fed to the heating element. The output might be a simple on/off signal, or it may vary continuously, reducing the power as the control point is reached.

6.6 Timed to perfection

As stated in a previous section, cooking is concerned with applying energy so that chemical changes can occur. Unlike laboratory experiments in chemistry, which usually wait for an end product, it is possible to take cooking too far. You only have to consider a simple meal like bacon, egg and chips.

Undercooked, the bacon is like rubber and difficult to chew, the egg will be runny (even the white part), the chips will be pale and hard; it will all be unpleasant to taste. Overcooked, the bacon is brittle, the egg is edible but even the yoke is hard, the chips are dark and dry and have lost most of their taste.

Experience tells you when these items appear to be properly cooked. You are unlikely to record the time, but keep a constant watch. The cookers in the local chip shop will be fitted with a timer with an alarm. The owner can leave the chips to cook while serving customers or preparing the next batch of chips.

By contrast we see very little change in the appearance of vegetables such as potatoes, carrots or peas while they are being boiled. Consequently we tend to watch the clock when cooking these items but usually test with a fork to check that they are just right.

Timers are not needed if the food doesn't cook too quickly and if it looks very different once cooked, although they can still be used as an *aide memoire*. Food that doesn't visibly change, such as boiled eggs, needs to be timed. Microwave cooking, which in many cases is extremely quick, has to be timed as a few extra seconds can completely ruin some foods.

There is, of course, a whole variety of timers. The simplest is the egg timer (Figure 6.8), which uses sand flowing under gravity between two glass bulbs. The limitations with this type of timer are that you cannot adjust the time and that you have to be watching to know when the time is up.

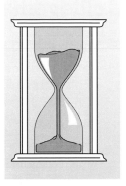

Figure 6.8
An egg timer

 What determines the time that an egg timer will measure?

The amount of sand and the size of the hole between the two bulbs.

At the next level of complexity is the clockwork mechanical timer. This has the advantages that the time is adjustable and a bell will sound to tell us when the time is up.

We now have available a range of electric and electronic timers. Electric timers are usually designed around a **capacitor** and electronic ones will use a **quartz crystal** to keep time. These are much more accurate than the clockwork ones available and are reliable enough to build into cookers to make them switch on and off automatically. Capacitors are discussed in the SLIPP unit *Physics Phones Home*.

Achievements

After working through this section you should be able to:

- explain the relationship between potential difference and current, and use the expression $V = IR$
- use the expressions $P = IV$ and $P = I^2R$, which combines $P = IV$ with $V = IR$
- describe the graph of the potential energy stored in a bond versus the length of the bond, and explain how it can lead to expansion on heating
- describe how bimetallic strips make use of thermal expansion.

Glossary

Automaton A machine or device that can alter some physical quantity (such as temperature, position or voltage) in order to remove the error between a measured value and a desired value.

Bimetallic strip A strip made of two metals, bonded side by side, which have different values of expansion coefficient. As the temperature changes the strip flexes.

Calorific value The energy obtained for a unit quantity of fuel.

Capacitor An electronic component, formed from two parallel plates separated by a dielectric (insulator).

Comparator A device that gives as its output the difference between two inputs.

Conventional current Imaginary current that flows from the positive to the negative terminals of a power supply. The charge carried would be positive.

Electromotive force (emf) A potential difference that produces current rather than the potential difference across a component due to a current. All power supplies have an emf, which is the potential difference at their terminals when no current flows.

Expansion coefficient The change of length per unit length for a 1 K change of temperature for a given material. The expansion coefficient itself is dependent on temperature, so care must be taken that the value being used is appropriate for the temperature range being calculated.

Ohm's law The current flowing in a conductor is directly proportional to the potential difference across it, as long as there is no change in its physical conditions, $I \propto V$.

Photophobia An extreme sensitivity to light.

Potential well A large dip in the curve of potential energy versus interatomic or intermolecular distance. It has a well-defined minimum value.

Power rating The official value for power transfer for an appliance.

Quartz crystal A crystal of the mineral quartz. The molecules change shape when a potential difference is placed across them and vice versa. This causes the whole crystal to deform. They can be used in loudspeakers and gas lighters. They can also be used as oscillators to control timers very accurately.

Resistance The ability of a material to restrict the flow of electrons in it.

Thermocouple A thermocouple is constructed by connecting a length of wire of one metal to one end of a length of wire of another metal. The free end of this is in turn connected to another length of the first metal. An emf can be measured between the two free ends of wire when the two junctions are at different temperatures.

Answers to Ready to Study test

R1

As water is heated the kinetic energy of the molecules rises and so ,therefore, does the temperature of the water, as $E - \frac{3}{2}kT$.

Eventually the molecules gain enough energy to overcome the bonds that keep them in the liquid state and become gas, which leaves the liquid. This happens at 373 K (100°C). So at normal air pressure water cannot exist as liquid above 100°C, and although we continue to heat the liquid the temperature remains constant. This energy received by the liquid causing it to vaporize is called latent heat.

R2

(a) Electrons are the negatively charged particles that orbit the nucleus of an atom.

(b) The other particles are protons and neutrons, which are both found in the nucleus.

(c) Protons are positively charged. The amount of charge on an electron is equal and opposite to that on a proton. The charge on an electron is in fact -1.6×10^{-19} C. Neutrons have no charge.

R3

Ammeters measure current, voltmeters measure potential difference. The ammeter should be used in series with the source and load, the voltmeter should be used parallel with the source and load. In order to measure the current flowing in the circuit, the ammeter has to be placed so that the current flows through it. Ammeters are designed to have as low a resistance as possible so that they do not affect the size of the current. A voltmeter measures the difference in the potential between two points in a circuit. It is placed outside the circuit under test and is connected only at the two points of interest (usually across a component like a resistor). They are designed to have extremely high resistances so that they draw negligible current from the circuit. An ideal ammeter therefore would have zero resistance while an ideal voltmeter would have infinite resistance.

R4

The ammeter would be placed in series between the source of current (e.g. a battery) and the resistor under test, the voltmeter will be placed across the resistor under test. You would then take a series of readings of current and potential difference. The resistance is the ratio of the potential difference across the resistor to the current flowing through it. (*Note:* Not all conductors obey Ohm's law, but all have the property of resistance.)

Answers to questions in the text

Q1

$$\Delta E_{el} = 250 \, \text{coulombs} \times 12 \, \text{volts}$$
$$= 250 \, \text{C} \times 12 \, \text{J C}^{-1}$$
$$= 3000 \, \text{J}$$
$$= 3.0 \, \text{kJ}$$

Q2

Light bulb, toaster, microwave and kettle. We would expect them to be in this order although it does depend on your particular appliances.

Q3

(a) Power, $P = IV$. But $V = IR$ and so, substituting for V,

$$P = I^2 R$$

alternatively, substituting for I,

$$P = \frac{V^2}{R}$$

(b)

$$P = I^2 R$$
$$= (4\,\text{A})^2 \times 60\,\Omega$$
$$= 960\,\text{W}$$
$$= 1\,\text{kW (to one significant figure)}$$

Q4

For the bulb:

$$60\,\text{J s}^{-1} \times 3600\,\text{s} = 2.2 \times 10^5\,\text{J}$$

For the iron:

$$750\,\text{J s}^{-1} \times 3600\,\text{s} = 2.7 \times 10^6\,\text{J}$$

For the heater:

$$2000\,\text{J s}^{-1} \times 3600\,\text{s} = 7.2 \times 10^6\,\text{J}$$

Q5

(a)

$$\text{Energy} = 40\,\text{MJ m}^{-3} \times 156\,\text{m}^3$$
$$= 6240\,\text{MJ}$$
$$= \frac{6240}{3.6}\,\text{kW h}$$
$$= 1733\,\text{kW h}$$

(b)

$$\text{Cost of gas supply} = 1733\,\text{kW h} \times 1.5\text{p}\,(\text{kW h})^{-1}$$
$$= 2600\text{p}$$
$$\text{Total cost} = \pounds26.00 + \pounds9.50$$
$$= \pounds35.50$$

Q6

Copper expands more than iron over any temperature change. So the copper should be on the outside.

If you think back to the beginning of this unit, you will realize what a lot of physics you have covered by looking at preparing and eating food from a different perspective.

To help you to appreciate how far you have come, look back through the list of achievements for each section. If you feel unsure about any of them, go over the relevant section(s) of this unit again. When you feel fairly confident about most of these achievements ask your teacher for the exit test for this unit. When you have done the test, consult your teacher, who has the answers and will probably wish to go through them with you. We hope you have enjoyed learning about the physics of food with this supported learning unit, and that you want to use more units in the series.

CONCLUSION

Resources and further reading

Adkins, C. J. (1987) *An introduction to Thermal Physics*. Cambridge University Press, Cambridge.

Auel, J. (1986) *The Mammoth Hunters*. Hodder & Stoughton, Sevenoaks. See also Jean Auel's Earth Children website: http://www.geocities.com/Athens/6293/auel.html

Bonington, C. (1976) *Everest the Hard Way*. Hodder & Stoughton, Sevenoaks.

Burgen, A. S. V. (1989) 'Is there a case for permitting the irradiation of food?, in Kurti, N. and Kurti G. (eds) *But the Crackling is Superb, An Anthology on Food and Drink by Fellows and Foreign Members of The Royal Society of London*. Institute of Physics, London.

Carey, J. (ed.) (1995) *The Faber Book of Science*. Faber and Faber, London.

Chambers Concise Dictionary of Scientists (1990) (compiled by Millar, D., Millar, I., Millar, J. and Millar, M.). W&R Chambers, Edinburgh.

Chemical Rubber Company (1974) *Handbook of Chemistry and Physics* (55th edn), p. E224, Chemical Rubber Company, Boca Raon, FL.

Collins Gem Calorie Counter (1995). Collins, London.

Denny, M. W. (1993) *Air and Water*. Princeton University Press, Princeton, NJ.

Earle, L. (1994) *Food Facts*. Boxtree, London.

Feynman, R. (1965) *The Character of the Physical Law*. BBC, London.

Good Housekeeping Cookery Encyclopedia (1985) (compiled by the Good Housekeeping Institute). Treasure Press, London.

Gordon, J. E. (1971) *The New Science of Strong Materials*. Penguin, Harmondsworth.

Tables of Physical and Chemical Constants (14th edn, 1973), originally compiled by Kaye, G. W. C. and Laby, T. H., now prepared under the direction of an editorial committee. Longman, London.

New Scientist, 'A taste for irradiated food: the public remains unconvinced by the mountains of evidence that the irradiation of food is safe. Minister are unperturbed' (1 January 1989, vol. 123, no.1671); 'Irradiated food for thought' (20 January 1990, vol. 125, no. 1700); 'Irradiated food – too hot to handle: the British government will soon present parliament with a bill to allow food to be sterilised by irradiation. But is the process safe and do we really need it?' (17 February 1990, vol. 125 no. 1704); 'Fried chicken: America allows irradiation of poultry with gamma rays' (12 May 1990, vol. 126 no. 1716); 'US bans "hormone free" milk label', Kurt Kleiner (26 February 1994, vol. 141, no. 1914).

Scientific American, 'The Einstein–Szilard refrigerators' (January 1997).

Smith, D. (1989) *Delia Smith's Complete Illustrated Cookery Course*. BBC, London.

Suzuki, D. (1993) *Inventing the Future: Reflections on Science, Technology and Nature*. Adamantine Press. (This book deals with issues like food irradiation – in hard-hitting text.)

Acknowledgements

Grateful acknowledgement is made to the following sources for permission to reproduce material in this unit:

Photographs and figures

p. 21: Basking collared lizard (*Crotaphytus collaris*) – Ardea London Ltd; p. 34: Sir Edmund Hillary with Norgay Tenzing on Everest – Royal Geographical Society, London; p. 34: A pressure cooker – Mike Levers; p. 38: Le Creuset cookware – Mike Levers; p. 39: Baked Alaska – Ken Field/BBC *Vegetarian Good Food* magazine; p. 45: James Dewar – Royal Institution collection; p. 46: A microwave oven – Mike Levers; p. 72: A modern coolbox and a traditional coolbox – Mike Levers; p. 74: Clipline plate heat exchanger – Controlled Communications Ltd/ Tetra Pak; p. 80: James Clerk Maxwell – Kings College London; p. 93: Abbé refractometer – Bellingham & Stanley Limited, Longfield Road, North Farm Industrial Estate, Tunbridge Wells, Kent TN2 3EY; p. 104: Cardboard milk carton – Mike Levers; p. 113: Thomas Young – Science & Society Picture Library, Science Museum, London; p. 121: 'Griffin makes a dramatic escape', illustration by Louise Strimpl, 1912 – Mary Evans Picture Library; p. 139: A cooking range – Mike Levers.

The authors and Management Group would also like to thank Kerry Parker, David Tawney and Liz Oliver for their helpful comments and advice whilst writing this unit.

Index

Abbé refractometer 93
absolute scale 14, 23
absolute zero 14, 23, 73
absorption bands, 47, 48, 50, 127, 130
absorption coefficient 47, 50
accelerated freeze drying 95
adenosine triphosphate (ATP) 22
ampere 141
antinodes 46, 50
atoms
    excited states 127, 130
    interatomic separation 60–1
    isotopes 82, 96
    transitions 127, 131
automaton 151, 154

bimetallic strip 147, 148, 152, 154
binding energy 59, 95
black body 42–3, 50, 123
blanching 95
boiling 30, 31, 66
    effect of pressure 32, 34
Boltzmann's constant 15, 23
bonds 57, 59, 95
botulism 139

calories 18–19, 23
calorific value 145, 154
capacitor 153, 154
carbohydrates 21
cardboard boxes 116
cellophane 116
cellulose 116
celsius 14, 23
centigrade 23
chemical potential energy 10, 23
chlorophyll 10
colour 82, 123
    food 77
    food packaging 119
    mixing 129
    printing inks 128
comparator 152, 154
conduction, thermal 26–9, 51

conductivity
    electrical 29
    thermal 27, 29, 51
conductors, heat 27
conservation of energy 10–11, 23
convection 37, 50
conventional current 140, 154
cooking 26–49
    pressure 30
    temperature control 138–9
    timers 152–3
coolbox 71–2
coulomb 140, 141
critical angle, total internal reflection 92, 95
cybernetics 151

Dewar flask 44
Dewar, James 45
dielectric constant 79
diet 18–20
dipole moment 47, 50

elastic constant 110, 130
elastic limit 110, 130
electric charge 140
electric current 140, 143
electric field 47, 51
electrical conduction 29
electrical energy 10, 140–5
electrical power 143, 144–5
electrical resistance 142
electromagnetic energy 42
    absorption 123–7
    absorption coefficient 47
    properties of 81
    spectrum 78, 96
    waves 78, 95
electromagnetic radiation see
    electromagnetic energy
electromotive force (emf) 150, 154
electronic states 126–7, 130
electronic transitions 126–7, 130
electrons, free 28–9, 51
emf see electromotive force
emulsion 82, 83, 95

energy 23
  binding 59, 95
  calories 18–19
  chemical potential 10
  conservation of 10–11
  definition 9
  electrical 10, 140
  food 18–20, 21–2
  gravitational potential 9
  heat 10, 11–12, 15
  internal 10–11, 59, 141
  joules 18–20
  kinetic 9, 10, 12, 14, 15, 24, 30–1, 141, 145–6
  light 10
  molecular kinetic 12, 14
  muscles 9
  potential 9, 10, 60, 68, 96, 145–6
  zero point 73
energy levels 130
  discrete 130
energy transfer 10–12, 15, 16–18, 26–9, 140–1
  conduction 26–9, 51
  convection 37
  electromagnetic radiation 42–3
  thermal radiation 41–4
entropy 17–18, 23
equilibrium 23
evaporation 30, 37, 50, 70–1, 72
excited state, atomic 130
expansion
  coefficients 147, 154
  solids 146–7
exponential decay 125, 130

farad 79, 95
fire 39
fluorescence 127, 130
food
  colour 77
  drying of 75–6
  energy store 8, 10, 18–20, 21–2
  freezing 62–4
  optical properties of 78
  packaging 104, 107–8
  preservation of 54, 56
  texture 78

free electrons 28–9, 51
freeze drying 76
freezers 72–4
freezing 62–4
frequency 95
  waves 79
fructose 116

glucose 21–2, 116, 118
glycation 123
gravitational potential energy 9, 24
gravity 9
ground state 131

HDPE see high-density polythene
heat 11–12, 15
  radiation 41–4
heat capacity 35, 51
  specific 36–7, 51
heat exchanger 72, 74–5, 95
heating, colour changes 41–3
henry 79, 95
high-density polythene (HDPE) 116
Hooke, Robert 111
Hooke's law 110, 131
hydrogen bond 47

infrared wavelengths 39, 42, 51
interatomic separation 60–1
internal energy 10–11, 24, 59–60, 141
isotopes, radioactive 82, 96

joule 18–20, 24

kelvin 24
kelvin temperature scale 14, 24
killowatt hour 145
kinetic energy 9, 10, 12, 14, 15, 24, 30–1, 141, 145–6
kinetic theory 57

latent heat 65, 96
Le Chatelier's principle 33, 51
light
  absorption 123–7, 130
  absorption coefficient 121, 122
  absorption factor 125, 130

dispersion 130
reflection coefficient 121
speed of 86–7
wavefront 84
light energy 10

magnetron 46, 51
Maillard reaction 123
materials
amorphous 118, 130
brittle 115, 130
crystalline 118, 130
deformation 109–11
ductile 115, 130
elastic 130
expansion 146–7
extension
elastic 110, 130
elastic limit 130
limit of proportionality 110, 131
plastic 110
ferromagnetic 80, 95
plastic 116, 131
polymeric 118
matter
particles 57, 59
phases of 56–61
Maxwell, James Clerk 80
melting 64–5
effect of pressure 32–4
metabolism 21–2
metal, extension 109–11
microwaves 46, 51
oven 46–8
mirrors 120
molecular kinetic energy 12, 14, 59–60
molecules
excited states 127, 130
speed of 16
transitions 127, 131

Ohm's law 142, 154
organic polymers 116, 131
ovens 37, 39

pasteurization 74–5
permeability 79, 96

permittivity 79, 96
phase
changes 32–4
diagram 32, 51, 77
of matter 96
phosphorescence 127, 131
photon 81, 96, 126
photophobia 154
Planck's constant 81
plastic bags 116, 117
plastic deformation 110
plastic materials 131
polymer 131
potassium-40 96
potential difference 140
potential energy 9, 10, 60, 68, 96, 145–6
chemical 10
gravitational 9
potential energy well 145–6, 154
potential well see potential energy well
power 141, 143
power rating 141, 154
pressure, vapour 31
pressure cooker 34–5
printing inks 128

quantum 81, 96
quantum mechanics 96, 126, 131
quartz crystal 153, 154

radiation
electromagnetic 42
heat 41–4
reflection 120
total internal 92, 95
refraction 84–94, 96
refractive index 78, 85–8, 93, 94, 96, 120
refrigerator 72–3
relative permeability 79
relative permittivity 79
resistance 142, 149, 154
resonant cavity 46, 51

saucepans 37, 38
SI units (Système International d'Unités) 14, 24
Snell's law 84

specific heat capacity 36–7, 51
specific latent heat
    of fusion 65, 67, 96
    of vaporization 65, 68–9, 72, 96
speed, molecular 16, 70
spray drying 76–7
standing waves 46, 51
Stefan's law 44, 51
strain 112, 131
stress 112, 131
sublimation 76, 96
sucrose 118

temperature 11–12, 14, 15, 16–18, 24, 31
    human body 21–2
temperature control 138
thermal conduction 26–9, 51
thermal conductivity 27, 51
thermocouple 150, 154
thermodynamics
    first law of 10–11, 23
    second law of 18, 24
    third law of 73, 96
thermometers 147–50
Thermos flask 44
thermostats 96, 138, 148–9
timers 152–3
toaster 148, 149

total internal reflection 92, 96
    critical angle 92, 95
triple point 32

vacuum flask 44, 46, 51
vapour 30, 51
    pressure 31–2
volt 140

watt 141, 143
wavelength 78, 79, 96
waves
    antinodes 46, 50
    electromagnetic 78, 95
    frequency 79
    microwaves 46, 51
    standing 46, 50, 51
    wavefront 96
Wein's displacement law 42, 51
Wiedemann–Franz law 29, 51

X-ray analysis 60, 97

Young modulus 112, 114–15, 131
Young, Thomas 113

zero point energy 73, 97